ALIVE
&
KICKING

ALIVE & KICKING

The true life story of an NFL star's battle with
ulcerative colitis, ostomy surgery, and hepatitis C

ROLF BENIRSCHKE
WITH MIKE YORKEY

Alive & Kicking
by Rolf Benirschke with Mike Yorkey

© 2016 by Rolf Benirschke

Print 978-1-944242-97-8

eBook Editions:
Adobe Digital Edition 978-1-944243-40-1 (.epub)
Kindle and MobiPocket Edition 978-1-944243-81-4 (.prc)

Printed by Friesens in Altona, Manitoba, Canada

If you're interested in making bulk purchases of *Alive & Kicking* and other books by Rolf Benirschke, please contact:

Rolf Benirschke
Legacy Health Strategies
12790 El Camino Real, Suite 300
San Diego, CA 92130
(858) 568-7555
www.rolfbenirschke.com

Cover and interior design by Catherine Thompson (phatphamly@yahoo.com)

Cover photo by Mark Frapwell

For more information on Rolf Benirschke, please visit www.rolfbenirschke.com.

DEDICATION

To my parents, Kurt and Marion Benirschke. You were always there, especially during my darkest hours.

And to my wife, Mary, whose love for me and our children, and for so many others, inspires me every day.

CONTENTS

A Note to the Reader

What you are about to read is a revised and updated version of *Alive & Kicking*, which was originally published in 1996.

This is my story of how I overcame ulcerative colitis and ostomy surgery to return to the National Football League as the placekicker for the San Diego Chargers, but what happened was really just a prelude of what was in store for me for the rest of my life.

I would imagine that you're holding this book or scrolling through your e-reader because you or someone you love is suffering from ulcerative colitis or Crohn's disease, or maybe you are facing ostomy surgery. If that's the case, you might be looking for some encouragement or a reason to believe that things can get better. I hope my experiences detailed in *Alive & Kicking* can give you the boost of confidence and heartening support you need and that you will come away convinced that your life is *absolutely* worth fighting for.

First, please know that you are not alone.

Currently, more than three million Americans live with debilitating intestinal ailments and more than 100,000 men, women, and children undergo ostomy surgery each year. But matter-of-fact statistics aren't comforting when it's *you* sitting in the doctor's examination room, waiting to discuss what lies ahead. Nor are numbers particularly consoling if you've recently had ostomy surgery and are still trying to figure out your new way of life with an ostomy appliance attached to your side.

Ostomy surgery is a traumatic event. I know. I've been there. But I'm here to tell you that it is *not* the end of your life, and the doubts you have about never being able to do the things you love are just that— they are doubts but they are *not* real.

When I was hospitalized in 1979, my life hung in the balance, and at one point, doctors braced my parents to expect the worst. But by the grace of God and great medical care, I survived two life-threatening operations six days apart and left the hospital weeks later knowing that I had been given an incredible present—the gift of life.

I'll admit that I had doubts about my future and what my life would be like. During my recovery, I was close to giving up many times. I believed I would never be able to engage again in any of the athletic pursuits I really enjoyed like playing tennis or skiing or going to the beach and body surfing. I was also single and doubted I would ever find a girl who would marry me. And playing again . . . there was no way in my mind that I would ever again kick in the NFL.

A dark cloud of discouragement hung over me during my recovery as I struggled to shuffle from my parents' home to our neighbor's mail box and back again . . . attempting to lengthen my walk each day by adding another mailbox to my route. I often wondered why I should even try, as everything seemed so hopeless at the time.

If you or someone close to you is about to undergo ostomy surgery, you likely have similar concerns of what your life will be like after the operation. You probably harbor many of the same dark thoughts I did—that you'll no longer be able to travel, participate in sports, be intimate with someone you love, or live a full and active life. If you're a young woman, you may fear that you'll never be able to conceive and bring a child into the world.

What I've learned is that *none* of those fears are true. In fact, having now communicated with literally thousands of ostomates over the years, I can tell you that you can return to *everything* you were doing before your operation—and feel healthy maybe for the first time in years.

From most of the patients that I've been fortunate enough to connect with, I hear that their illness has changed them, that they came out the other side with a different outlook on life. They are most appreciative of family and friends, recognize they have been given a second chance at living, and are determined to seek more life in their days as opposed to more days in their lives. They take stock of their situation and seem more determined than ever to follow whatever the passion is that consumes them.

Now, more than thirty-five years later, I have the benefit of hindsight. I can unequivocally tell you that my ostomy surgery was worth it. Not only did it save my life . . . but it allowed me to return to doing *everything* I did prior to my operation. I urge you to stay the course and press forward with whatever challenge you're facing, and I hope that *Alive & Kicking* can inspire you to pursue your passion and discover the indomitable spirit that I believe God has hidden within each of us.

But there's another audience I would like to welcome to *Alive & Kicking*— those with hepatitis C. As you'll learn later in these pages, I discovered quite by chance—following a routine life insurance test in 1998—that I had become infected with the virus when I received 78 units of blood during my life-saving ostomy surgery nearly twenty years earlier.

The news about my hepatitis C infection not only rocked my world but also caused me to fear for the welfare of my wife, Mary, and our four young children. I felt embarrassed, dirty, and ashamed, but I knew I had to confront the issue head-on, much like I had done when I was a scared, twenty-four-year-old football player fighting to stay alive.

But I'm getting ahead of myself here. You'll learn more about all of this and the rest of my story as you turn the pages of *Alive & Kicking*. I hope you enjoy the journey, and I thank you for joining me.

1

REDEMPTION

Even before I heard Coach Don Coryell call for the field goal team, I was jogging onto the moist turf of the Orange Bowl. The score was tied 38-38 in a game that a panel of ESPN experts would later vote as one of the best games in National Football League history. "The Epic in Miami," they call it today.

The Chargers and Dolphins had battled in muggy heat and humidity for more than four hours, and it had finally come down to this—a chance for me to ice the game with a 29-yard field goal 14 minutes into overtime. I was twenty-six years old and in my fifth season as an NFL placekicker.

I didn't hear the capacity crowd of 75,000 rise to their feet and scream at the top of their lungs. I was in my own little world, oblivious to everything around me. The Dolphins fans were exhorting their team to block my field goal attempt or pressure me into missing. The fans knew that if my kick was good, the Dolphins season was over.

For nearly five quarters, the roaring crowd had witnessed San Diego and Miami playing a game of "Can You Top This?" with two offenses that couldn't be stopped. The two clubs had generated more than 1,000 yards in total offense and produced more great plays than most fans see in an entire season.

But the game didn't start out that way. We had jumped out to a huge and usually insurmountable 24-0 lead in the first quarter as

Chargers quarterback Dan Fouts riddled the Dolphins secondary. Every play we called seemed to work. We were so far ahead that the guys on our bench were already talking about playing the Cincinnati Bengals in the AFC Championship game the following week. As far as we were concerned, the fat lady was singing. This game was history.

That kind of thinking can be fatal, especially when a Hall of Fame head coach like Don Shula was prowling the opposite sideline. In a gutsy move, Shula decided to bench his struggling starting quarterback David Woodley in favor of Don Strock, a veteran backup. Strock brought a hot hand to the Dolphins offense, throwing a quick touchdown strike, then getting the team close enough for a field goal.

The Dolphins comeback had begun. Just before halftime, Shula caught everyone by surprise. He called for a "hook and ladder"—the kind of school-yard play that kids diagram in the dirt.

Trailing 24-10, Strock threw fifteen yards downfield to a well-covered Duriel Harris. As our secondary closed in to make the tackle, Harris quickly lateraled to a trailing Tony Nathan. The play worked perfectly, and our defense was completely fooled. Nathan pranced down the sideline untouched, and 10 yards before the end zone, he raised the ball high into the air, taunting the nearest Chargers pursuer.

The Miami crowd went absolutely nuts! The roar was so deafening that I couldn't hear a teammate swear in disgust three feet away. Even though we were still ahead 24-17, we had clearly lost the momentum. Stunned and angry, we limped into the locker room at halftime with our heads down. I wondered how we were going to regain our composure and preserve our fragile lead in the second half.

My question was answered when Dan Fouts, the last player off the field, stormed into the locker room. We were all sitting there, staring at the carpet, our eyes glazed over. The wind had been completely taken out of our sails.

Fouts, the most competitive player I'd ever been around, was absolutely livid. He stormed into the locker room, reared back, and fired maybe his most effective pass of the day, hurling his helmet the length of the dressing room. The Chargers helmet caromed off a locker, nearly hitting receiver Wes Chandler.

Our leader had our attention.

"What the @#$% is going on?" screamed Fouts. "Get your @#$% heads out of your @#$% butts. We're still leading this thing. They haven't stopped us yet! We're not going to let this bunch of @#$% take this @#$% game away from us. No @#$% way!"

Dan's words woke us up, and he had a point. The Dolphins defense hadn't stopped us at all, and if we could just get a little help from our defense, we could still win this game.

"C'mon guys, Dan's right," yelled Big Russ Washington, our 300-pound offensive tackle. "We've come too far this season to let these @#$% stop us."

The mood in the locker room quickly changed, and you could feel the team's resolve return. We were ready to battle again.

BACKS TO THE WALL

The second half, as many football pundits still say today, was one of the best in NFL history. The Dolphins caught us at 24-24, but we answered and took the lead at 31-24. But they caught us again and went ahead with two touchdowns to claim the lead, 38-31. Miami then threatened to put the game out of reach in the last five minutes, driving down to the Chargers 21-yard line. But our defense finally came through when Gary "Big Hands" Johnson stripped Dolphins fullback Andra Franklin of the ball and we recovered.

It was now up to Fouts and the offense to respond. We took advantage of the reprieve and marched 82 yards for a touchdown with just 40 seconds to go. With everyone celebrating on the sideline, I still had to kick the extra point to tie the game. It seemed like I was the only one on the field who knew this wasn't a gimme, especially given how torn up the field was. Although I was very nervous, I made the kick to tie the score at 38-38.

On the ensuing kickoff, the coaches instructed me to squib-kick the ball to keep it out of the deep receivers' hands and prevent a long runback. That strategy backfired when the Dolphins recovered at the 20-yard line and ran the ball to their 40. Since our defense had hardly slowed Miami the entire game, it only took a few plays for Miami to get into field goal range. With four seconds to go, Shula waved in Uwe von Schamann to attempt a game-winning 43-yard field goal.

It was then that our special teams coach, Wayne Sevier, had a brilliant idea: Insert 6'6" tight end Kellen Winslow at the center of the field goal block team. Kellen had already played his heart out all afternoon, having to be carried off the field several times because of exhaustion, cramps, and dehydration. Now he was being called on to try to bail us out one more time.

With the fans on their feet, screaming and anticipating a last-second victory, Kellen somehow willed his exhausted body high into the air and blocked von Schamann's kick.

Overtime!

GOING FOR THE WIN

As the captains went out for the coin toss, I was keenly aware that overtime games were sudden death and generally decided by a field goal. I knew I had to be ready.

We got the ball first, and before anyone could catch their breath, Fouts had us on the Miami nine-yard line. On second down, the Chargers coaching staff—not wanting to risk a fumble—decided to go for the game-winning kick.

"Field goal unit!" barked head coach Don Coryell.

I ran onto the field with my holder, Ed Luther, but only half of the kicking team followed us. They hadn't heard Coryell over the roar of the crowd, nor had they anticipated the call for a field goal on second down. For several chaotic moments, confusion reigned as a dozen Chargers ran on—and off—the field. Meanwhile, I tried to count helmets as the play clock ticked toward zero.

Should I call time-out I wondered? It was all too rushed, and we weren't really ready.

"Eddie, we're not set!" I yelled.

"We'll be okay," he said hurriedly. "We're close enough. Just kick it."

Ed looked toward the center and called for the snap. The ball was hiked, he caught it and set it down, and I started toward the ball like I had done ten thousand times before.

But we were out of sync, and I hadn't really gotten settled. I watched in disbelief as my 26-yard kick sailed wide left. I couldn't believe what had just happened.

I had missed. I had failed to control the situation and had let my teammates down. The Miami fans went crazy, cheering wildly while I headed back to the bench—the loneliest walk of my life. All I could think about was how hard my teammates had fought for this game and how I had just blown it for them.

A couple of the guys came up and tried to encourage me. "Hang in there, Rolf, we're going to get you another chance," said one. "Keep your head up," said another. But they say that all the time. In my mind, I knew I wouldn't get a second chance.

I stood stunned while a renewed Dolphins team took over and quickly marched the ball back into Chargers territory. Behind the Miami bench, I could see their kicker von Schamann warming up, kicking into the practice net. Surely he wouldn't miss a second time.

When our defense finally stiffened, Shula sent in von Schamann to boot a 34-yarder for the win. It was agonizing to watch and feel so helpless.

Once again, it looked like our season was over. Would I have to live with my miss the rest of my life? I wanted to turn away, but I couldn't.

The crowd seemed to quiet and hold its breath as the field goal unit lined up. All eyes were fixed on the Dolphins' kicker, certain he would finally end this marathon and seal their remarkable comeback. The pressure was almost unbearable. I watched the snap and the ball placed in a perfect hold. Uwe started his approach, but he appeared to rush the kick. He didn't hit it well, kicking it low and into the outstretched arms of defensive end Leroy Jones. The ball bounced harmlessly away.

It couldn't be! Really? We were still alive, and now I had to get my head back into the game. We had a chance!

I immediately began stretching and jogging up and down the sidelines. Was this game ever going to end? Now it was Fouts' turn to go back to work. Key catches by Winslow, Chandler, and Charlie Joiner quickly moved us down to the Dolphins 12-yard line. Once more Coach Coryell yelled "Field goal unit!" Ironically, it was second down again.

Well, it's nice he still has faith in me, I thought as I jogged back onto the field, focused like I've never been before. *I've got to make this. I can't let my buddies down again.*

As the field goal protection unit huddled for the last time, I searched the torn-up field for a good spot to kick from. No one said anything to me. My teammates had learned long ago that I preferred to be left alone, to focus and concentrate on the task at hand.

Surprisingly, the butterflies were gone. I couldn't hear the crowd or the taunts the Dolphins were yelling at me from across the line. I couldn't see the Miami defensive line jumping up and down trying to distract me. I was totally prepared for this moment.

Twenty-nine yards. Pretty straightforward for an NFL kicker. This time, everyone was ready. The snap was perfect, Ed's placement was where it should be, and I knew right after I hit it that the kick was good.

As I watched the ball fly high over the crossbar, a deep feeling of satisfaction came over me. The game was over, finally. The Miami fans had been treated to a wild ride, but now the Orange Bowl had become eerily quiet. In fact, the only noise was coming from our bench and a small band of supporters that had made the long trip from San Diego.

As I turned toward our sideline, Chargers players jumped for joy and hugged one another, while others simply fell to the ground, overcome with exhaustion and emotion. It really was over this time. We had won!

Upstairs in the broadcast booth, NBC's Don Criqui and John Brodie told a nationwide audience that they had just been treated to something very special.

"If you didn't like this football game, then you don't like football," Criqui gushed. "This was one of the most exciting NFL games ever played."

Postgame Pandemonium

Our dressing room was a madhouse. The pendulum of emotions we had experienced—opening up a huge lead, seeing it disappear, and then having to fight with everything we had to finally win—left everyone physically and emotionally spent.

Louie Kelcher, our mammoth defensive tackle, wrapped Dan Fouts in a bear hug that threatened to squeeze the life out of him. Running back Chuck Muncie stood on a bench and alternately swirled a towel and exchanged high fives. But most of the sweat-drenched players were too tired to celebrate and were only able to sit and take it all in.

Suddenly, the lights were extinguished. The laughter and other sounds of jubilation slowly quieted.

"Men . . . the Lord's Prayer," commanded Coach Coryell. Delivering those few lines of Scripture was a Chargers tradition after every game—win or lose. This time, however, the words of the prayer never seemed so fitting or so special. I joined four dozen weary but grateful men as we got on our knees in the darkened room.

When we began with *Our Father, who art in heaven,* I stopped reciting. I took a moment to thank God in my own heart for giving me a second chance to kick the game-winning field goal . . . but even more, for allowing me to survive a pair of life-threatening surgeries six days apart just two years earlier. I know I could have easily died during one of those surgeries.

When we finished the prayer, I climbed onto the stool in front of my locker, bent over and put my head in my hands, and remembered for a moment the anguishing time when my health odyssey had begun.

We had just lost to the New England Patriots. I boarded the team plane heading back to San Diego but was weak, dizzy, and fighting to keep my balance as I made my way to my seat in the back.

I slumped into my seat and tried to get comfortable, ignoring as best I could the pain that was knifing through my abdomen. I tried to sleep but awoke several times with terrible cramps that reminded me I needed to go to the bathroom. I struggled to get out of my seat and headed back to the lavatories where I shut the door and looked at my pale face in the mirror.

I was spaced out, and I knew it. I sat on the tiny toilet and let it go. I felt the usual liquid exit my rectum, and then I stood up to see what it looked like. It was all blood!

This was not the first time blood had passed my bowels; I had been hemorrhaging rectally off and on for a year. But this time the bloody mess in the stainless steel toilet frightened me. The pain had intensified, and I knew something was really not right.

I limped back toward my seat but before I could get there, I suddenly collapsed in the aisle. My world went black, and the next thing I knew Jeff West, our punter, was gently shaking me.

"Are you all right, Rolf?" he asked urgently. Jeff put his hand to my forehead. "My God, Rolf, you're burning up."

Jeff turned around and yelled, "Someone get the doctor! Hurry! He's hot as hell!"

It was only a minute before one of the Chargers team physicians rushed to my side. He saw my flushed face, sized up the situation, and stuck a thermometer under my tongue.

"He's 103 degrees!" he exclaimed.

The team doc quickly ordered several of my stunned teammates to carefully lay me across three seats and then wrap me in several blankets. Although my body may have been burning up, I was freezing. My teeth started chattering, and my whole body began to shake.

I learned later that a Chargers official asked the pilot to relay a message to my parents back in San Diego that I was very sick and might have to be hospitalized upon landing. They were asked to meet the plane when we landed at 9:30 p.m.

The ending of the Lord's Prayer brought me back to the present. The lights were turned back on, and the celebration resumed.

Our equipment manager, Sid "Doc" Brooks, began picking up our sweaty away jerseys and mud-stained yellow pants with the distinctive lightning-bolts down the side. Doc knew we were about to be mobbed by reporters, but he also knew an NFL locker room was an open invitation for hangers-on to walk off with some "souvenirs."

After a few minutes, when it was just us enjoying the moment, Rick Smith, our public relations director, made his way to the heavy orange door and placed his hand on the lock. "This is it, guys," he announced. "Ready for the media?"

"Hold it, Rick," yelled Louie Kelcher. "Give us some more @#$% time. They can wait."

Finally, the pounding on the door forced Rick to open up, and a herd of sports journalists, TV reporters, cameramen, and sound people stampeded in. They immediately surrounded Fouts, Winslow, Joiner, and other stars of the game. Before long, a smaller army of media types found me in front of my locker. They formed a semicircle three-or-four deep.

The energy and assaultive noise level was like nothing I'd ever been a part of. Bright lights shone in my face, making it hard for me to see. Guys with pencils and pads and tape recorders started yelling questions.

"Did you know it was good when you hit it?"

"Did anyone say anything to you after you missed the first kick in overtime?"

"What would you have done if you had missed the second one?"

"Did anyone say anything to you before you went out for the last kick?"

"Was that the most pressure you've ever faced?"

"Is this your biggest thrill?"

I answered each question patiently and thoroughly, knowing that it was the media's job to replay each morsel of information to a world anxious to see, read, and hear every little detail.

Since there were far too many members of the media to interview any one player at a time, the journalists would move from one player to another in packs. That meant every few minutes a new group of reporters and cameramen would appear. Once in place, they peppered me with the same questions.

"Did you know it was good when you hit it?"

"Did anyone say anything to you before you went out for the last kick?"

"Was that the most pressure you've ever felt?"

"Is this your biggest thrill?"

I repeated the same answers, and then the reporters slipped away to the next player while a new group took their place.

"Did you know it was good when you hit it?"

"Did anyone say anything to you before you went out for the last kick?"

"Was that the most pressure you've ever felt?"

"Is this your biggest thrill?"

I couldn't help but smile as I answered the last question for the umpteenth time.

"Yes, it was the biggest thrill I've ever felt . . . in a football game."

In a football game.

None of the reporters caught the significance of those last four words, but I didn't expect them to. You see, I was thrilled just to be alive and kicking.

2

THE EARLY YEARS

G rowing up in the Ivy League town of Hanover, New Hampshire,
where Dartmouth College is located, I had the chance to play
lots of different sports, but I certainly never expected to end up in the
National Football League.

My brother, Steve, and I always participated in whatever sport was
in season: soccer, ice hockey, ski racing, baseball, or tennis. Kicking a
football wasn't even on the radar because in the fall, soccer and football
were played at the same time. We always chose soccer, partly because
one of the boys who lived down the street—someone we admired—was
a soccer player, but mostly because we enjoyed the constant movement
and creativity the sport required.

To our father, Dr. Kurt Benirschke, a medical school professor
at Dartmouth, sports were recreation. Athletics were meant to keep
us physically fit and teach us lessons about teamwork, discipline, and
hard work; beyond that, we were always reminded that sports were for
fun. To make sure we never got too engrossed in athletics, we never
owned a TV, which meant Sunday afternoons in the Benirschke home
were *not* spent watching NFL doubleheaders.

Dad was always doing something productive, and when you learn
about his background, you'll understand why. He grew up in Adolph
Hitler's Germany during the 1930s and 1940s, and when World War
II broke out, he was a medical student at the University of Hamburg.
Dad was forced to interrupt his studies to serve in the medical corps.

He hated the war, and while working as a medic in the Battle of the
Bulge region in Belgium, Dad caught a break. He contracted hepatitis,

which put him in the hospital and almost killed him. Ironically, the hepatitis likely saved his life because the virus got him off of the front lines and out of the war.

When the war finally ended, Dad wanted to complete his medical studies and looked forward to becoming a doctor. Unfortunately, his father had passed away while he was gone. Since my father was the only son, his mother expected him to forget medicine and return home to run the family laundry business.

But Dad was not cut out for that line of work, and he knew it. He realized that the only way he could pursue his dreams in medicine would be to strike out on his own. So, in 1949, he dropped a bombshell and announced to his mom and two sisters that he would be leaving the Fatherland and immigrating to the United States. Although he didn't know a word of English, he was determined to become a doctor despite the disapproval he was sure to experience.

His family didn't take him seriously at first, betting him that he'd be back in six months. With their doubt and criticism ringing in his ears, he arrived by freighter in New York City with only a few dollars in his pocket and a fierce desire to succeed in his adopted country. He knew only one person in New York City, a distant relative named J.J., who helped arrange a job for him as a delivery guy for a Manhattan publishing house.

Kurt spent three months running errands, working on his English, but never forgetting his dream. When he felt confident his English was good enough, he applied and was accepted to an internship program in Teaneck, New Jersey. It was there that Kurt met a pretty German-speaking nurse named Marion Waldhausen. They soon discovered they had much in common.

Born in the U.S. to German parents, Marion was raised in Berlin. Unfortunately, their family's home was bombed early in the war, and she, her mother, and her brother were able to flee the country for the U.S.— a minor miracle in itself. When Marion began her nursing career, she quickly became a popular young lady at the hospital where Dad found himself working. Marion Waldhausen didn't lack for suitors.

But the young nurse found herself drawn to the solid young doctor from Germany with boundless energy and a genuine concern for his patients. They went out a few times, but because they were both so busy at work, most of their interaction was professional.

Things looked increasingly hopeless that the two of them would ever get together when Kurt was accepted to Harvard Medical School, where he would complete his residency. He moved to Boston, and although he and Marion tried to maintain their friendship, their busy work lives and the distance made it difficult. The only way they communicated was through letters and infrequent phone calls.

As fate would have it, Marion developed a serious kidney infection that would require major surgery. When Kurt learned she planned to be operated on in Teaneck, he was horrified. He immediately arranged for her to be transferred to Boston, where she could receive better treatment. Of course, Kurt could also keep a close eye on her, as well.

The extensive surgery required that Marion be hospitalized for a month in Boston. Kurt, ever the attentive doctor, managed to drop in several times a day to make sure this "patient" was recovering well.

One afternoon, shortly before she was to be released, Marion had some news for Dr. Benirschke.

"When I'm better, Kurt, I've decided to move to Montana," she shared. "Mom moved out West a little while ago, and she wants me to join her."

"Montana is a long ways away, isn't it?" asked Kurt, still unsure of his U.S. geography.

"Yes, it is," said Marion sadly.

Later that day, Kurt bumped into the chairman of the Pathology department who had been watching this promising relationship develop. Kurt's boss immediately sensed something was amiss by the long look on Kurt's face.

"What's wrong?" he asked. "You look like you're carrying the weight of the world on your shoulders."

"Marion just told me she'll be leaving for Montana soon," replied the young resident.

"Really? What are you going to do about it?"

"I'm not sure," Kurt confessed. "I really like her and would like to ask her to marry me, but I don't have any money."

The Pathology chairman shuffled his feet. He had visited Kurt's apartment and seen the orange-crate chairs and meager furnishings. "If she loves you, money won't matter," he offered. "Besides, you're one of the best residents we've ever had, and you have a bright future in medicine. But more than that, if you don't ask this girl to marry you now, you'll never see her again."

Buoyed by this encouragement, Kurt proposed before Marion had time to leave for Montana, and she accepted. Marion did travel to Montana, but instead of living there, she informed her mother of the good news. Kurt followed a short time later in his $50 car, driving more than 2,000 miles to formally ask for her hand.

KIDS ARRIVE

Kurt and Marion married in 1952, excited to start a family. They didn't waste time. Steve was born a year after the wedding, and I arrived on the scene two years later on February 7, 1955. Our sister, Ingrid, joined us in April 1956.

Four years later, Dad was offered the chairmanship of the Department of Pathology at the Dartmouth Medical School in Hanover. He was just thirty-seven at the time—the youngest chairman the department had ever had.

Growing up in a college town was a special experience. Hanover was a small community where everyone knew everybody and where crime was virtually nonexistent. Walking or riding our bicycles home from grade school was always an adventure. We often stopped off at Dartmouth's huge athletic practice fields to watch whatever team was in season. I loved shagging balls for the soccer team, and I'd kick missed shots back to the players. My friends and I had plenty of fun doing that. I also discovered I had a pretty good leg.

During the winter, the snow and cold temperatures didn't keep us indoors. Instead, we learned to ski on the local hills. As we got bigger and better, we graduated to the steeper slopes of Stowe and Killington, where we began to race.

When I was in fourth grade, I discovered another winter sport that

I really liked—ice hockey. The first cold snap of the season was exciting because that meant the neighborhood gang could head over to the frozen lakes on the golf course or Occum Pond for pick-up hockey games. Occum Pond was the best since it was almost a mile long with fast, clear ice, and where the college maintained a rink. For me, there was nothing more exhilarating than passing a puck back and forth with a couple of friends while skating the entire length of the pond.

We were always trying to find time to skate. Every now and then we would sneak into the indoor rink on the Dartmouth campus. I can remember climbing through an open window at 9 p.m. and turning on the lights for an hour of pick-up hockey with my buddies. We'd do anything for "ice time" and would play until the campus police would find us and kick us out.

To get in shape for hockey, most of us played soccer in the fall. The two sports are similar in tactics and strategy, and I soon developed a passion for the game. In ninth grade, I made the high school varsity soccer team, although I was still quite small for my age. I was looking forward to three more years on the team when suddenly, my life turned upside down.

COAST TO COAST

In the middle of my freshman year, Dad changed our lives forever when he announced that he had accepted a teaching job in San Diego.

Dad, who had been the chairman of the Pathology department for ten years, had been instrumental in developing the program into one of the best in the country. But he was a restless man, always looking for new challenges. The idea of a new teaching position at the University of California at San Diego with a high-powered group of research scientists intrigued him.

The UCSD campus was located in La Jolla, a sleepy seaside town about fifteen miles north of San Diego. Mom had grown weary of the long winters in New Hampshire, and the thought of never having to shovel another snowy walkway in her life brought a smile to her face. Sunshine always seemed to put her in a good mood, so when school ended in June, we packed up the car for the trip west. Mom may have been the happiest member of the family, but Steve, Ingrid, and I were sad at what we were leaving behind. We didn't know anyone in California, and we were really uncertain of what our new lives would be like.

The move to California may have been the toughest on my older brother Steve. He had just finished his junior year and was one of New England's top junior skiers, routinely beating racers who would end up skiing on the U.S. Olympic team. In addition, he would be leaving his high school friends and forced to finish his senior year in an unfamiliar school.

The move was difficult for me, too. My bantam hockey team had just won the state championships in New Hampshire, and I quickly learned it would be impossible to keep playing hockey in San Diego. I also discovered that La Jolla High didn't even have a soccer team. Ingrid, who was going into ninth grade, had the easiest transition, but I can assure you the long drive to the West Coast wasn't the most enjoyable car trip the Benirschke family had ever taken.

That first winter without hockey skates and downhill skis was a real adjustment for us. Since San Diegans see snowflakes once a century, I had to stifle a laugh when I heard the locals complain about the mercury dipping into the forties. But we made the best of it and quickly got used to going to the beach during our Christmas break.

Besides not offering the sports we were used to playing, I had another problem. I was little. I mean *really* little. I was a skinny five feet four inches and weighed just 112 pounds when I started my sophomore year.

Despite my size, I was still fairly coordinated. My gym teacher, Gene Edwards, saw some potential in me. The potential he saw, however, wasn't so much my athletic ability—it was my lack of weight. You see, Edwards was the wrestling coach (and the football coach), and he didn't have anyone to wrestle at the 112-pound weight class.

I had barely heard of the sport, and I certainly had never seen a wrestling match in my life. But for some reason, I allowed myself to be talked into joining the team.

What a mistake! In my first match, the referee had barely uttered "Wrestle!" when I was on my back, pinned in just seventeen seconds. It was a humiliating experience, but I vowed to finish what I had started, so I completed the season.

Things began to look up, however, when a bunch of transplanted East Coasters and a few foreign-exchange students got together and formed the school's first soccer team during the winter of my junior year. Besides allowing me to play a sport I truly loved, soccer also gave me a chance to gracefully end my wrestling career since both sports were played during the same season.

One afternoon after soccer practice, a couple of my friends who played on the football team brought out a football and talked several of us into a field goal kicking competition. Unbeknownst to us, the head football coach was leaning against the gym, watching. I found out later that my friends had arranged for Coach Edwards to be watching from a distance.

A spirited competition broke out. After kicking a few field goals at close range, we moved back further and further. When you missed, you were out. Slowly, guys dropped out until it was just me at 50 yards. I drilled the kick and had a good laugh with my buddies.

That's when I noticed Coach Edwards strolling over in my direction. "Rolf, how would you like to kick for us next year?" he asked with a big smile.

Not again! The memories of my embarrassing wrestling career under his leadership were fresh in my mind, and I wasn't certain I was ready to try something new like high school football. Coach Edwards was old school, which meant he thought placekickers should play another position as well as participate in all practice drills. Although I had grown some since my sophomore year, I was still skinny at five feet eleven and 140 pounds. The idea of getting crunched by 225-pound linemen in tackling drills was not the way I wanted to spend my senior year at La Jolla High.

"Ah . . . I don't know," I told Coach Edwards. "I've never really played football. I'm not sure it's for me."

Coach didn't persuade me that day, but he didn't give up either. Every time he saw me over the next few months, he would ask me if I wanted to kick on the team. He even got some of his players to put the squeeze on and told them to tell me that I could just kick and not have to play any other position . . . thinking that might be the reason I was still hesitating.

The more I thought about his offer, the more intriguing it sounded. The part about kicking field goals sounded relatively easy. I knew that I had a strong leg, and I had watched the new soccer-style kickers on television and understood their technique was just like kicking a goal kick in soccer. I believed if you could kick a soccer ball correctly, then it wouldn't be too big of an adjustment to kick a football through the goalposts. It was the other aspects about place-kicking—the snap and the hold and the timing and the rushing linemen—that I wondered about.

Finally, after lots of talking with my friends on the football team, I agreed to become La Jolla High's first kicking specialist my senior year.

Coach Edwards gave me a bunch of footballs to practice with over the summer and told me to be ready for August, when the team would go through two weeks of double-sessions to get ready for the season. I ended up spending that summer working at a grocery store, bagging groceries, and my free time was spent at the beach followed by late-afternoon kicking sessions at the high school, trying to figure this all out.

Summer ended all too quickly, as it always seems to, but that meant it was time to see if all my practicing was enough to prepare me for what was to come. Our season-opener was a night game. I was excited but nervous and still trying to feel comfortable wearing all of the strange-fitting pads. It was a whole lot different than kicking field goals in shorts. I wondered how everything would all work.

Late in the first half, our offense stalled at the 20-yard line.

Before I knew what was happening, I heard Coach Edwards yelling, "Field goal unit!" As if in a dream, I trotted onto the field for my first-ever field goal attempt. My shoulder pads felt funny as they bounced around, and my head swam in my football helmet. Poor lighting made the goalposts look really far away.

"C'mon, Rolf, you can do this," encouraged my holder, Don Gravette, knowing this was all new to me. He gave me a smile and slapped me on the helmet. "Just pretend it's practice."

The team broke the huddle and lined up on the ball. I counted off seven yards from the line of scrimmage and put my kicking pad down; it would be a 37-yard kick. Suddenly everything seemed to slow down, just like in the movies. Don called for the ball to be snapped, but it seemed to take forever for the ball to reach him. As he caught the football and placed it on the kicking pad, I instinctively moved toward the ball, planted my left leg and swung my right.

I met the ball with my instep and followed through, lifting my head to watch the ball clear the line and lazily climb into the dark night toward the goalposts. The ball hung for what seemed the longest time as it sailed easily over the crossbar. A feeling of deep satisfaction shivered through my body. I had made it!

I jogged off the field like I had been kicking field goals all my life, but my heart was pounding from the excitement. I couldn't stop grinning. Teammates rushed out to congratulate me, slapping my loose helmet and pounding my shoulder pads.

My kicking career had begun.

RECRUITMENT

I kicked a record number of field goals that year, mostly because La Jolla High's offense didn't score many touchdowns in the red zone and partly because we had an assistant coach who convinced Coach Edwards that we should kick on fourth downs instead of going for it.

I went 12-for-14, including a 45-yarder that got me named "Prep Athlete of the Week" by the *San Diego Union* newspaper. Remember, this was the early 1970s, and soccer-style kicking was a relatively new thing at the high school level. Pioneers like Pete Gogolak, Garo Yepremian, and Jan Stenerud were just beginning to replace the traditional toe kickers in the pros and making kicking a real weapon.

When the season was over, I was surprised to be named to the All-CIF first team. Suddenly, football coaches from Stanford, UCLA, Cal Berkeley, San Diego State, and other schools began calling about me. I wouldn't exactly say I was heavily recruited, but there was some genuine interest.

One of the calls came from Coach Don Coryell, already a local legend at San Diego State. Coryell invited me to the 52,000-seat San Diego Stadium (now known as Qualcomm Stadium) to watch the Aztecs play their final game of the season. For a high school kid, this was Big Time, especially because I was allowed to bring a buddy to share in the experience.

I invited a teammate, and as we were escorted into the locker room before the game and introduced to several San Diego State players, I felt like a wide-eyed little kid. From there, we were ushered upstairs to the press box, where I got my first chance to watch sportswriters in action—at the buffet table.

Everything was so new and seemed so big and professional and was definitely a world I knew nothing about. I took it all in, never imagining that this would all come full circle, and I would be playing here in this stadium—in front of many of these same reporters—just a few years later.

The phone calls from major college football coaches amused my family. We never really took them seriously because the real world, Dad reminded me, wasn't kicking a football around on Saturday afternoons. An education in science—not sports—was what college should be all about.

Dad didn't pressure me on what I should study, though. He just wanted me to work hard in college and apply myself. As for my major, I liked science and the idea of studying endangered species, but I wasn't really sure what I wanted to focus on. My brother was pre-med at UCSD and intent on following Dad into the field of medicine, but I knew I didn't want to become a doctor. I toyed with the idea of becoming a park ranger or working as an ornithologist (someone who studies birds), but I didn't know if I could earn a living in either of those professions.

When I discussed my options with my parents, we talked about my passion for wildlife, which had been sparked from our early days in Boston. Dad had built out our cellar with a bunch of cages to study the breeding behavior of several different species of marmoset monkeys. I loved going down to feed them and watch them play and jump around. Those were special times that I treasured.

We were a family that also collected butterflies and moths. Whenever we traveled anywhere by car, Dad packed several butterfly nets in the trunk. We would stop frequently at open fields that were full of flowers and catch whatever species of butterflies were flying around. When we arrived back home, we would spread and pin the wings of the butterflies and then lay them out in picture frames that we hung on the basement walls.

On weekends, I often accompanied Dad to his lab on campus, where he would explain the various projects he was working on. They ranged from his studies on human twins, to trying to understand why armadillos have identical quadruplets every time they have offspring, to looking at the chromosomes of endangered species.

Dad had become a leading authority on twins and the placenta and was increasingly curious about the diversity in the animal world. When we moved to San Diego, he convinced the San Diego Zoo to set up a research center known as CRES (Center for Reproduction of Endangered Species) that would be dedicated to understanding and preserving endangered wildlife.

When my high school graduation arrived in June 1973, Dad surprised me with an unusual gift. That summer, he gave me the opportunity to attend a Wilderness Leadership School outside Durban, South Africa. I would join five other students from around the world to learn and experience man's relationship with the environment by spending twenty days living and studying in several game reserves in the area.

The school's founder, Ian Player (brother of golfing legend Gary Player) believed that if he could bring young adults into the bush and expose them to nature like they've never experienced before, it would profoundly impact the rest of their lives; and they would become sensitive to the issues surrounding wildlife when they became older. He was right. The Wilderness Leadership School would have a profound effect on me, and I still count that experience as one of the most meaningful in my life.

Our small party of six students spent almost three weeks hiking the game trails around three game reserves in South Africa, learning about the wildlife and the Zulu tribe that inhabited the area. Camping at night meant taking turns standing watch and keeping the all-important fire lit. Since only one of the game guards had a rifle, it was frightening being the only one awake at 2 a.m., silently stoking embers and wondering what man-eating animals were lurking beyond the light of the fire. The game preserve was home to lions, cheetahs, hyenas, wild buffaloes, elephants, and more. During my entire time in the wild, it became very clear to all of us that *we* were the visitors.

I was fortunate to spend several more weeks after the school at the Umfolozi Game Reserve, where I helped with an important white rhino project. The rhinos, which were in danger of becoming extinct, were proliferating in this special reserve because it was a perfect habitat, and its small size made it difficult for poachers to get to the protected rhinos.

A small group of conservationists had learned how to dart (tranquilize) these amazing animals and bring them back to holding pens called *bomas*, where they would acclimate for a month or so. Then the rhinos would be returned to their original breeding areas to repopulate.

PLANS ARE MADE

When I returned from South Africa, I knew what I wanted to study—Zoology. I had become fascinated with endangered species and loved my experience in the bush, so even though I wondered if I could make a living studying wildlife, I knew I had to find out. The best school for Zoology on the West Coast was at the University of California at Davis.

"Dad, I want to go to UC Davis," I announced shortly after getting home. The state university was located twenty miles west of Sacramento in Northern California. The small city of Davis, population 25,000, was completely focused around the school . . . much like what I remembered from my childhood days growing up in the Ivy League town of Hanover.

"That's a good school," Dad said. "Davis has a medical school, a veterinary school, and even a primate center. I am up there fairly often and work with some bright scientists who love it there."

By now, I wasn't thinking much about football and knew the science classes required for a Zoology degree would be tough and require a lot of studying. My thinking was that I couldn't afford the time to play sports and keep my grades up, so I didn't even look into whether or not UC Davis had a football team. Although I enrolled with no intention of playing football, an unexpected phone call from Jim Sochor, UC Davis' head football coach, changed all that.

Coach Sochor called my dorm room about a week after school started. After introducing himself, he said, "I received a call from a coach I know at the University of Southern California. He told me that they had been recruiting a good kicker, but he turned them down to enroll here at Davis. The USC coach was miffed at why somebody would turn down the Mighty Trojans to go to little ol' UC Davis, so he pretty much assumed I must've been doing something illegal to make that happen. When I explained I hadn't recruited a kicker and that no kicker had walked on to play, the USC coach became even more puzzled. I finally asked him for the name of this kicker, and he gave me your name. Now that I've found you, perhaps you can tell me why you didn't go to USC, and, even more importantly, why you didn't come out for the team here."

I was completely unprepared for this call. I tried to explain to Coach Sochor about my dad and his feelings about sports, and the fact that I wanted to study Zoology, which meant a lot of study time and attending labs. Besides, I said, I had only played one season of high school football and didn't know if I was really good enough to kick at the college level.

Coach listened quietly until I was done explaining things. "Well, you must have some talent, or USC wouldn't have wanted you so badly," he said. "Why don't you come out for a week and see if you like kicking for us? Then we can talk about it."

I didn't have to think long. "Thanks for tracking me down, Coach, but I don't think football is in my plans."

He thanked me for my time, but that wasn't the last I heard from Coach Sochor. It turns out that Coach could be a pretty persuasive guy. After several more phone calls, I agreed to give kicking a try and ended up playing on the freshman team. They already had a senior kicker on varsity, and that was fine with me. I was able to manage my school-work, make a bunch of great friends, and carry out the transition from high school to college fairly easily.

After returning to Davis for my sophomore year and participating in the two-a-day training camps, a dilemma developed. While I did enjoy place-kicking, being a specialist on a football team wasn't the same as playing soccer, where you are an integral part of the team and continually part of the action. I'd gotten to know many of the UC Davis soccer players when I played in intramural soccer leagues during the winter and spring quarters of my freshman year. I realized I really missed the sport and was also good enough to play college soccer. My friends on the soccer team put a lot of pressure on me to join them on the varsity team.

The problem was that soccer and football were both fall sports, so I would have to quit football if I wanted to play soccer. I wrestled with what to do and how to tell Coach Sochor, who was counting on me to kick for the varsity squad. Our practice fields were right next to each other, so while we were practicing in full pads in the sweltering 100-degree heat, I would watch my soccer friends on the adjacent grass field, running around in their shorts and no shirts, having a blast.

The draw to play soccer grew stronger and stronger until one day, a few days before our opening game, I decided to bring up my dilemma with Coach Sochor. I explained how I felt and told him that I was considering quitting football.

He nodded understandingly. "Tell you what, Rolf," he said. "Let's play the upcoming game this Saturday night, and we'll talk about it Monday."

I didn't see any harm in that, so I agreed. When Saturday rolled around, all of us on the football team were excited to play our first game of the season, and we ended up destroying our opponent. I had a good game with plenty of chances to kick and loved contributing to the win.

On Monday, I walked into Coach Sochor's office and was surprised to find Will Lotter, the soccer team coach, also sitting there.

"Will and I have been talking," Sochor began, "and we think we've come up with a solution that will make everyone happy. What would you think if we 'share' you this season? Would you like to play for both teams?"

The idea completely blindsided me. Of all the possibilities, I certainly hadn't considered this. But how could I play both sports in the same season? There had to be schedule conflicts. And what about the guys on both teams? What would they think?

"I'm not sure," I answered hesitantly. "The last thing I would want to do is set myself apart from my teammates or let one of you down."

The two coaches explained why they liked the idea. Will Lotter said he felt they could really use a scorer like me and that I'd only miss a few minutes of soccer practice each day to kick footballs. Besides, he felt that by sharing me, I might help raise the visibility of the soccer team.

Jim Sochor gave his blessing because he knew how much I loved soccer and wasn't willing to risk losing me. He also felt that, by training with the soccer team, I was also getting stronger. He told me that I only needed a little time kicking with a snapper and holder to be prepared for the games.

It didn't take me long to say yes, although I had some doubts as to how it would all work and what my teammates would think. There was also the question of my studies and having to tell Dad what I was doing. When I did inform him, he was skeptical at first, but he said he was willing to support me as long as I kept up with my studies.

It was a crazy schedule, but it worked and I loved every moment. Teammates on both teams were supportive and seemed to enjoy the craziness as well. The next three years would turn out to be a lot of fun, as we had great teams in both sports. It wasn't lost on me that if I had accepted a scholarship to one of the bigger schools, I would have never been allowed to play two fall sports at the same time and would've missed out on some special memories.

The arrangement did, however, make for some interesting Saturdays. It wasn't unusual for me to compete in a soccer match in the afternoon, shower, grab a sandwich, change into my football gear, and then play a night football game. Road games were more difficult because sometimes I would have to jump into the car and drive an hour or two or get flown to the football game later that evening.

One occasion, however, almost turned into a disaster.

The soccer team was playing in the All-Cal soccer tournament in Santa Barbara. During the last game of the three-day event, I scored the winning goal in the consolation final. Immediately after the final whistle, I was whisked to the Goleta airport, still in my soccer uniform sweats, to catch a short flight to Los Angeles. A connecting flight put me into Sacramento thirty minutes before the football game that night.

I worked it out so that my roommate would pick me up at the airport with two Jack in the Box hamburgers and drive me to the stadium. I ate while he raced across town to Sacramento State College, where the football team was playing that night. Sac State was a crosstown rival, so this was usually the biggest game of the season.

We arrived at the stadium just before kickoff, but the security guard outside the locker room wouldn't let me in, not believing my story or that I was even a football player. Meanwhile, I could see Coach Sochor through the fence pacing the sidelines, looking around anxiously and wondering if his kicker was going to show.

"But I'm a player," I protested to the security guard. "You gotta let me in. Look, here are my kicking shoes. I'm just late for the game."

He wasn't buying it. Fortunately, one of our trainers saw what was going on and came over to vouch for me. The guard finally opened the door, and I rushed into the locker room to change into my football uniform as quickly as I could. I missed the opening kickoff, but I got into the game in time to kick three field goals in the first quarter. Those field goals were the difference in a thrilling game that we ended up winning by five points.

My Saturdays were almost comical at times, but I was sure enjoying the ride. I often wondered, *Was this really happening?*

But more importantly, would it last?

3

THE NEXT STEP

Although I kicked pretty well at Davis, I was focused on helping the soccer and football teams win games while trying to keep up with my studies and enjoy my college experience. I didn't have much time for anything else and certainly never entertained any serious thoughts about kicking in the NFL. But the summer before my senior year, I started receiving letters from quite a few professional teams. I began to wonder: *Could I kick in the NFL?*

The impersonal form letters from NFL coaches were quite humorous to me. Dallas Cowboys coach Tom Landry wrote, "An outstanding football player such as yourself usually watches his college career wind down to a close with mixed emotions. You may be experiencing feelings of accomplishment, frustration, and relief. But in your case, you may be feeling a sense of deserved optimism for a bright future in the National Football League."

Yeah, right. While I admired Tom Landry, he must not have realized that football at non-scholarship UC Davis, a Division II school, was quite a bit different than kicking at football powerhouses like Alabama or Michigan or USC.

When Draft Day came the following spring, I didn't have any real expectations. I learned later that several teams were actually quite interested in me but were reluctant to use a draft choice on a kicker. Even before the draft concluded, several teams called and tried to sign me as a free agent.

It turns out that the Oakland Raiders had been following my progress and decided to spend their very last pick on me. I was taken in the twelfth and final round of the 1977 NFL draft—the 334th player out of 335.

No Mel Kiper, Jr. Back Then

Every year when the NFL draft comes around in April, I chuckle at the differences between the drafts of the late '70s and Draft Day today. In this day and age, the NFL Combine is where the projected top picks are invited to run and jump and lift and be scrutinized by scouts and general managers prior to the draft. The players' stock rises and falls as tidbits of information are circulated among the ever-present hordes of journalists who love to speculate on who will be taken in which round and by which team.

All of this leads up to NFL Draft Day, which usually takes place at Radio City Music Hall in New York City, where ESPN and NFL Network analysts spend two days trying to explain what the next team "on the clock" might do.

Today, there are only seven rounds, which means I wouldn't have been drafted and likely wouldn't have given the NFL much thought. Although there was a good chance I would've been pursued to sign as a free agent, I probably–with strong encouragement from my dad–would've passed on the NFL and entered graduate school. How different my life would've been!

Although I was graduating on time with a B.S. degree in Zoology, I didn't get accepted into the UC Davis Veterinary School, where I had hoped to go. Instead, I was put on a waiting list and encouraged to apply the following year. In the meantime, I did get accepted into several graduate school programs that were appealing to me, so I faced a dilemma. What was I going to do?

The more I thought about my options with the Raiders, the more I figured, *What the heck? Why not see what pro football is all about?*

This would be a once-in-a-lifetime opportunity. If I didn't make the team, at least I would have some interesting stories to tell after moving on with my studies.

COLORFUL CHARACTERS

Back in 1977, the Raiders were the reigning Super Bowl champs. They were the feared Silver and Black with such personalities as Kenny "The Snake" Stabler, Jack "Hitman" Tatum, and Otis Sistrunk, who, as one football pundit described him, had graduated from the "University of Mars." Colorful characters, all of them, and *very* talented.

It was traditional for all first-year players to report to training camp a week ahead of the veterans. Remember, I was a wide-eyed, twenty-two-year-old rookie from little UC Davis, where our biggest crowds were about 8,500, if you counted the cows in the nearby fields. We certainly never played on national television or before 100,000 screaming fans jammed into Michigan's Big House or the Los Angeles Coliseum. *Was I good enough to compete with these guys?* I didn't know.

When the veterans finally reported, the mood in camp changed perceptibly. The big boys were back in town. We rookies suddenly felt like insignificant kids as the veterans reunited for the first time since their big win over the Minnesota Vikings in Super Bowl XI just six months earlier. It was fun to see how strong the players' bonds were, and all of us young guys dreamed about earning a spot on the team so we might experience the same thing one day.

Inside the locker room, the dressing stalls were numerically ordered to match our jersey numbers. I was assigned jersey number 6. Next to me was Ray Guy, number 8, one of the best punters in the history of the NFL. One locker down was legendary quarterback Kenny Stabler with his familiar number 12. He was "The Man," and everybody knew it.

When I walked into the locker room that first morning, I was startled to find Stabler already suiting up. I had spent my college years watching this guy perform his magic with the Raiders. He was a gutty competitor, the master of the two-minute drill, and someone you could never count out. Now he was dressing just a few feet away from me. The moment was kind of surreal, and I wasn't sure how to act. What should I do?

Careful not to make eye contact, I quietly dropped my bag next to my locker and began to change. I hadn't finished unbuttoning my shirt when Stabler, a grizzled good-ol' boy from Alabama, looked over and reached out to shake my hand. "Hey, Rolf!" he drawled. "How ya doin'?"

Did I hear right? Kenny Stabler was talking to me . . . and actually knew my name? I wasn't sure what to say.

"I'm fine, Mr. Stabler. Nice to meet you," I stammered back.

Kenny smiled at my formality. "Hey, I'm not that old. Please call me Ken. We're teammates now. I've read a lot about you, and we're excited you're here."

Wow! Really?

John Madden was the Raiders coach back then, before he became a famous color commentator on *Monday Night Football* and the guy behind the *Madden NFL* video games. Madden had a reputation for not liking rookies *or* kickers—which made me just about his least favorite player on the team. It was nothing personal; he just didn't care for players who didn't get their uniforms dirty.

Madden seemed to enjoy making life miserable for kickers, and he was famous for his little "tests." My first exam came one week into training camp. As morning practice was coming to a close, Madden pulled the whole team together.

"As you all know," announced Madden, "we end each practice by running ten 100-yard wind sprints. Today, we're going to find out how good our rookie kicker is. Benirschke, you've got one shot from 45 yards. If you miss, everyone runs. If you make it, everyone hits the showers."

I was totally unprepared for this. *Why didn't he give me some warning?* I felt my heart begin to pound as 100 players started screaming and yelling . . . at me! My legs felt like jelly, and I could hardly breathe. It was almost 100 degrees, and the players did *not* want to run wind sprints . . . and they let me know what would happen if I missed.

"Hey, rookie, you better not miss this @#$$% kick!" yelled John "Tooz" Matuszak.

"Miss this, and you'll be walking back to Davis," chimed in Ted "The Stork" Hendricks.

Madden cleared the field except for the defense and the field goal unit. Then he spotted the ball. As if taking pleasure in the situation he had created, he looked at me and blew his whistle. The countdown had begun. I was still trying to quiet my nerves as I searched for a good spot on the torn-up field to place the ball.

With the players going crazy on the sidelines, my holder, backup quarterback Dave Humm, took a knee seven yards behind the line of scrimmage. We had already become friends in camp, and I had relied on him not just to make good holds, but also for moral support and guidance. Once again, he had the right words of encouragement. "You can make this sucker," he said quietly.

As I paced off the steps and lined up the kick, the noise level rose. I knew why Madden was doing this, but I still hated it. Thinking about what he was doing changed my fear to anger. *I'm going to show this guy*, I vowed.

As I began the routine I had developed in high school, the distracting noise seemed to fade away. I was in my own world now, comfortable and in control. The ball was snapped, and I watched Dave catch it, put it down, and spin the laces. At the same time, I was already moving toward the ball. I planted my left foot and kicked with my right . . . effortlessly. The ball went spinning end-over-end toward the goalposts and easily cleared the crossbar. I made the kick!

The players whooped and hollered, ecstatic that they didn't have to run wind sprints . . . and started heading toward the showers. I was relieved Ted Hendricks wasn't going to kick my butt all the way back to Davis, and I also loved the adrenaline rush from coming through when I needed to. I gave Dave Humm a pat on the shoulder pads and a nod of thanks for his good hold. That was cool!

I like to joke that making that kick is one reason why I'm alive today to tell you this story. But seriously, that end-of-practice field goal was hugely important to me because making that kick, under that kind of pressure, gave me the confidence that I was good enough to compete for a job in the NFL.

Unfortunately, Madden wasn't done with his fun and games with me. He made me go through that same agony many more times before training camp was over. I despised him for what he was doing and the pleasure he seemed to derive from putting me in that situation, but I knew he was preparing me for the kind of pressure NFL kickers face every Sunday.

For that, I was begrudgingly thankful.

THE WAIVER WIRE

The Raiders training camp was loaded with veterans, and I was one of three kickers fighting for a job when camp began. My competition was Fred Steinfort, who had been drafted in the third round the previous season, but who'd injured his leg partway through the season; and Errol Mann, an accurate old-timer who had filled in admirably for Fred and kicked for the Raiders for the remainder of the season, including the Super Bowl. By the final preseason game, though, Steinfort and Mann had both been released, and I had the job!

Even though I had beaten out two veterans, I learned that in the NFL, nothing is for certain.

It turns out that there was an obscure rule back then that was intended to keep teams from stockpiling talent. The rule required every team to have two players on their final 45-man roster who had "cleared waivers," meaning every other NFL team had the option to claim them if they wanted to. Because the Raiders were so deep in talent, they were having a hard time deciding which two players they wanted to try to have clear waivers so they could be resigned.

With this dilemma in mind, team owner Al Davis and Coach Madden, the brain trust of the Raiders, gambled that I—a little-known kicker from UC Davis—wouldn't be claimed. Their plan was foiled, however, by the San Diego Chargers, who had scouted me in the preseason and were looking for a kicker.

When I got the call that I had been waived and then claimed by San Diego, I couldn't believe it. The truth was, I was devastated. I had just endured nine weeks of training camp and passed all the tests thrown my way. I had, like all rookies, sung my college fight song at dinner—a bunch of times. More than that, I had earned the respect and friendship of a great group of guys. In my mind, I had won the kicking job with the defending Super Bowl champions . . . and now I was being told I had to leave. I was suddenly no longer a Raider. What had happened just didn't seem fair.

Although I was going to play in my hometown of San Diego, I was also joining a last-place team and players I didn't know. When I climbed into my green '62 Volkswagen Beetle and left the Bay Area for the nine-hour drive south, a huge emptiness filled my stomach.

SIGNING ON

I drove all night to San Diego, arriving at my parents' house at around 4 a.m. Four hours later, I was up and on my way to San Diego Stadium. After parking my car and checking in at the security gate, I was directed to an elevator that would take me to the Chargers offices. I was carrying my football cleats and the rest of my gear in a small box. The receptionist greeted me with a smile.

"Young man, who is the delivery for?" she asked politely, noticing the box.

"No, this isn't a delivery. This box is mine. I'm looking for Coach Prothro."

"I'm sorry. He's getting ready for a team meeting in fifteen minutes."

"I know. I believe I'm supposed to be in that meeting."

In order to make room for me, the club released veteran kicker Ray Wersching. I was cheaper, of course, and signed for $26,000 that first year—tall cotton for a kid out of college, but much smaller than a single NFL game check for players today. The Chargers were in disarray when I arrived and just two years removed from a terrible 2-12 season. What I didn't realize, however, was that the team had a very successful draft following that dismal season and that those young players were maturing and ready to come together.

Unfortunately, we started the season without quarterback Dan Fouts, who was holding out for a better contract. Our opening game was ironically against Oakland, where just five days earlier I had been part of the team. As we lined up for the National Anthem before the game, I could tell the Chargers were really intimidated by the reputation of the big, bad, defending Super Bowl champions. For me, though, being at the Oakland Coliseum was like coming home. I knew everybody on the opposite sidelines and only a few players on my new team. It was surreal.

Turns out the Chargers had good reason to feel intimidated because we were totally outclassed that day. I kicked the opening kickoff but never got back on the field. Our offense never crossed midfield, meaning I never got remotely close to trying a field goal.

Things wouldn't get much better for the struggling Chargers. Eight games into my rookie season, I was one of the worst kickers in the NFL. I was still adjusting to kicking field goals without a tee, the narrower goalposts, and the intensity of pro football. The team also had a lot of areas that needed attention, and it seemed like our special teams were almost an afterthought. It wasn't unusual for me to get a bad snap or a breakdown in protection, resulting in a bobbled hold or blocked kick. Since the Chargers special teams weren't very special, we were regular features on the *NFL Bloopers* films.

As one disappointing game followed another, I found myself wondering what I had gotten myself into. The way it was turning out, each week was a new chance to embarrass myself on national television. Not only did I feel like I was making a fool of myself, but my father became the unwitting target of our team's poor play.

This pro football thing was a whole new world for Dad. When I was selected in the twelfth round by Oakland, a medical colleague called him from Boston and excitedly said, "Congratulations on your son getting drafted!"

"What?" replied Dad, not fully understanding. "I thought the draft had ended years ago."

Of course, Dad was thinking about the military draft during the Vietnam War and had no idea there was a draft held by the NFL for the top-talented college players.

When I first started playing for the Chargers, Dad suddenly found doctors, nurses, and orderlies he didn't know stopping him in the hospital where he worked and asking him to give me their best. "Let Rolf know that we're behind him all the way," they'd say. "We're excited he's a Charger, and we'll be watching."

Dad had a hard time understanding why everyone was making such a big fuss about his son playing such a foolish game. He didn't think much more about it, but when I started spraying kicks, friends and colleagues suddenly made things uncomfortable for Dad. They began avoiding him in the hospital hallways, not wanting to make eye contact or engage him in conversation, and he noticed. The awkward interactions, though, inadvertently forced him to begin learning about the game, and that was a good thing.

Meanwhile, I was thinking different thoughts. *What am I doing trying to be an NFL kicker? I didn't go to school for this. Maybe I'm not really cut out for professional football.*

It was then, quite by chance, that I received my first fan letter. For some reason, a twelve-year-old boy from Ft. Wayne, Indiana, decided to write and encourage me at a time when I was at my absolute lowest.

As I opened the letter that had been placed in my locker, I couldn't imagine why anyone would be writing me. Then I read the first sentence. "Dear Rolf. My name is Dean Meier, and I think the Raiders made a mistake when they cut you," the young boy wrote.

I almost laughed out loud. Based upon my early performance so far, I was pretty sure the Raiders were *glad* I was kicking for San Diego. They were probably feeling fortunate that the Chargers had called their bluff and claimed me off waivers.

"I know things haven't gone quite like you would have hoped in San Diego," he continued.

That's the understatement of the year, I thought. *Doesn't this kid know I'm one of the worst kickers in the league?!*

But then he added, "I believe in you, and if you just hang in there, things are going to work out."

I smiled at his optimism. Then I folded the letter and put it back in my locker. Then it dawned on me. There was a twelve-year-old boy out there who actually knew who I was, cared how I performed, and took the time to encourage me with a letter. Amazing.

Our next game was at home against—irony of ironies—the Oakland Raiders. The Raiders were hot and headed back to the playoffs; the Chargers had a 4-5 record and were going nowhere. To make matters worse, both our starting and backup quarterbacks—James Harris and Bill Munson—had been injured the previous week and would be unavailable for Sunday's game. We were going to have to go with a rookie QB named Cliff Olander. Our prospects were not good, and everybody was expecting a blowout.

On Sunday morning as I was dressing for the game, I couldn't help but think about Dean's letter—"I believe in you, and if you just hang in there . . . ." His words rang in my ears as I jogged onto the field for warm-ups.

The Raiders fought valiantly, but on this day, our defense played magnificently before a wild sellout crowd. Our offense did just enough to get me in position to kick two field goals. We won 12-7!

If you add the score up, however, you will realize I missed a PAT—it had been blocked, in keeping with the tenor of the season—but the difference was the two field goals I had kicked. We had pulled off the biggest upset of the year and won a game against our biggest rivals—a win that would help turn the Chargers franchise around!

A few days after the Raiders game, I received a second fan letter from my new friend. I slowly tore open the envelope. On a piece of yellow-lined paper, Dean had written simply, "See, I told you so. If you just hang in there, things are going to work out."

As I read those words, a smile crept across my face. He was right. I'm embarrassed to tell you today that it took a twelve-year-old boy to teach me an important lesson about life: *Even though we may not understand why things are happening, it is our responsibility to always hang in there . . . because things change.*

I couldn't help but write Dean back, and we started a pen-pal friendship that continued for the rest of the season. He'd write me before every game, and I'd reply on Monday right after we played. As it turned out, I didn't miss a kick for the rest of the year and finished kicking twelve consecutive field goals, breaking the club record and solidifying my position on the team.

Dean and I continued to exchange letters for several years. He explained that he had begun to follow me because it was his dream to become a placekicker one day. We arranged to meet before a game in Detroit one time, and I was able to thank him and his family and explain how much his letters had meant to me. I know it was a special day for him . . . but it was also *very* special for me.

Dean Meier, wherever you are today, you were a twelve-year-old boy who did something that I'll always remember. You gave me a lift when I needed it most, and for that I'll never forget you.

4

Storm Clouds

I opened the door to Doc Brooks' home and stepped inside.

Doc, the Chargers longtime equipment manager, had invited several of the single players over for a *Monday Night Football* cookout. It was the day after our season-opening win against the Seattle Seahawks in my second season, and I was still on a high. I had tied a Chargers team record by kicking four field goals in our 33-16 victory.

I walked in and said hi to my buddies huddled around the TV set. During a commercial break, one of the guys wondered if it was true what our head coach, Tommy Prothro, had asked me before the Seahawks game. We were playing inside the enclosed Kingdome, and I had come back to the bench after practicing kickoffs. Coach Prothro, who liked to manage all the variables, actually asked me which way the wind was blowing and what direction I would prefer to kick off.

Not sure how to reply, I smiled and looked up at the vast ceiling. "Coach, there doesn't seem to be much wind in here today."

My teammates howled upon hearing the story, and then we made a beeline for the food. Doc's wife, Jeri, always laid out a wonderful spread, and she always made us feel like part of the family. On the dining room table were French fries, tossed green salad, corn on the cob, fresh bread, and the best barbecued chicken you've ever tasted.

Doc, a dutiful husband, was just finishing a few more chicken breasts on the barbecue as we worked our way through the buffet line and took our seats near the TV. For a bachelor, it didn't get much better than this.

A short time later, however, a wave of painful cramps suddenly rippled through my abdomen. I doubled over in pain, and for a long minute I couldn't straighten up. The game was getting exciting, so nobody noticed me get up and go to the bathroom—for the third time that hour. *Must be that fast-food burger I ate at lunch time,* I thought.

After relieving myself, the stomach cramps subsided for several minutes and I returned to watching the game. Thankfully, no one had seen my painful grimaces. I shrugged off the lingering cramps, figuring it had to be mild food poisoning or the start of a flu bug. Several teammates had been feeling under the weather, including Coach Prothro. Something was making the rounds, and I thought maybe it was getting to me.

A couple of days later, however, I still wasn't up to par and was getting concerned. My teammates had gotten well, and even Coach Prothro said he was feeling much better. I decided to see the team doctor, who— after hearing my symptoms and examining me—also reasoned that it was probably the flu. I didn't press the issue. I had already learned in professional sports that you didn't want a reputation of being prone to injury or sickness. I loved what I was doing, and the Chargers would have to carry me off the field before I pulled myself out. Besides, our next game was against the arch-rival Raiders—at home.

When game time came around, things had gotten worse. I was running a steady low-grade fever, and the pain in my gut was now pretty constant. Even worse, my diarrhea had become more unpredictable. I was worried that once the game started, I wouldn't be able to leave the bench to get to a bathroom if I needed to. With our high-powered offense, you never knew when the special teams coach would yell "Field goal unit!"

Late in the first quarter, I had a chance to kick a field goal but slipped on the dirt infield and pulled the short kick wide, breaking a string of thirteen straight without a miss. (We shared the stadium with the San Diego Padres baseball team, which hadn't completed their season yet, so the dirt infield was not sodded over.) Then I flat-out missed an extra point.

The errant kicks weighed on my mind as we nursed a 20-14 lead late into the fourth quarter. I was worried about Oakland's reputation for heroic comebacks. With only a few minutes to play, Raiders quarterback Kenny Stabler and the offense took over the ball deep in their own territory. Would he put together another one of his patented game-winning drives?

I almost couldn't watch as the Snake wasted no time and surgically drove the Raiders down the field into scoring position. With just nine seconds remaining, he had his team with a fourth-and-goal on our nine-yard line, down by six points. The Raiders had to go for the touchdown, and our fans knew it. They stood and made as much noise as possible, hoping to distract Kenny and the Raiders. In the face of a ferocious rush, Stabler dropped back to pass but found everyone covered. He tried to avoid the pressure by stepping out of the pocket and scrambling toward the goal line. But he wasn't fast enough, and a couple of Chargers caught him behind the line of scrimmage. Just as he was about to be pulled to the ground, Stabler intentionally sidearmed the ball toward the end zone.

The ball bounced twice—like Vegas dice—into the arms of Raiders fullback Pete Banazak, but Banazak was still a good five yards from the end zone. He was hit immediately, but just before *he* went down, Banazak intentionally pitched the ball toward the goal line, where Raiders tight end Dave Casper kicked it over the goal line and fell on the ball in the end zone. Incredibly, the referees raised their arms, signaling touchdown!

Both benches erupted, and 52,000 Chargers fans rained boos of disbelief and anger on the Raiders and the referees.

"He can't do that!" screamed Prothro, who had to be restrained. "That was an incomplete pass! The play should have been dead!" The enraged fans continued to boo in complete disbelief at what they had just witnessed. The refs could have opened their rulebook and called just about anything: incomplete pass, illegal forward pass, illegal batting the ball, or intentional kicking the ball forward . . . but they didn't.

Keep in mind that in 1978, there was no instant replay. Today, this travesty of justice would be overturned in a New York minute. But back then, we were stuck with the call on the field.

After conferring for several minutes—without the benefit of looking at a televised replay—the referees allowed the touchdown to stand. The Raiders quickly tacked on the game-winning extra point, and we slowly trudged to the locker room with a devastating 21-20 defeat. We couldn't believe what we had just witnessed. We were convinced this one had been stolen from us, and everyone in the stadium felt the same way.

Stabler's resourcefulness would live in infamy and become known as the "Holy Roller" play. To this day, what happened that afternoon still irks Chargers fans, and those who were there or watched the game on TV and will never forget the feelings that went along with the incredible sequence of events they witnessed that afternoon.

The Holy Roller play would lead to the NFL changing the rules the following season and disallow forward fumbling in the last two minutes of a game. But there was no changing what happened, so we had to live with a bitter loss to a hated divisional rival—and that stunk.

That week, much frustration was vented in the "Letters to the Editor" page in the *San Diego Union* sports section. Most letter-writers criticized the referees who, by unanimous verdict, blew the call . . . make that several calls. But one fan correctly pointed out that the refs' decision wouldn't have mattered if the Chargers had someone who could kick short field goals and extra points.

I put the newspaper down. It felt like someone had kicked me in my already tender stomach. The fan was right, and I knew I had cost us the game.

THE FIRST OFFICE VISIT

The next day, Mom was concerned about how I might be feeling after the game. After chatting for a few minutes, she invited me over for dinner. Mom's German cooking was the best. I loved her *Wiener Schnitzel*—a breaded and fried veal cutlet—and she was always supportive and seemed to know just what to say, especially after a bad game. Maybe some home cooking would help me forget about what had just happened and ease some of the pain.

As I walked into the house I had lived in while going to high school, I found Dad opening mail at the kitchen table.

"How's it going, Rolfie?"

"I don't know, Dad. Never mind the Raiders game, I just don't feel well."

"Are you still running a fever?"

"Yes, but the worst thing is the constant pain in my abdomen."

"You still having diarrhea?"

"Yeah, and what worries me is that it's not getting any better . . . and it's bloodier."

Dad stared off into space for a moment.

"We need to get to the bottom of this," he said matter of factly.

"What do you mean?"

"I mean you need to see a specialist. I can set you up with an appointment with the head of the gastroenterology department at UCSD. I'll call him in the morning."

The next day Dad arranged for me to see a doctor. I'll call him Dr. Jack Diamond, though that isn't his real name. From the first moment I shook hands with him, I did not connect with the man. He never looked me in the eye, and his uncertain manner didn't instill any confidence in me. Dad said he had a good reputation, but his indecisive manner proved to be frustrating for me.

He started poking here and pressing there, and then he drew blood for some tests. Man, I hated needles! When he was done with his exam, Dr. Diamond closed his file and told me to not to eat the rest of the day. His final instructions were to return the next morning for an X-ray series. They would do an "upper GI," also known as a barium swallow to see if they could find out what was going on.

Later that night, I asked Dad, "What's a barium swallow?"

"It's a procedure that requires you to drink a milkshake-like liquid that is radiopaque. As the barium progresses through your digestive system, a series of X-rays are taken that allow the doctors to examine the lining of your intestinal tract and see if there are any irregularities."

When I arrived the next morning, a nurse asked me what flavor "milkshake" I wanted.

"I'll try strawberry," I answered. Just one sip from the cold tin told me this concoction wasn't prepared at Dairy Queen. The heavy liquid tasted metallic, and it was all I could do to get it down.

As the barium shake slowly passed through my intestinal tract, Dr. Diamond and a technician took an X-ray every few minutes, looking for any abnormalities. It wasn't long, however, before the awful-tasting liquid intensified my intestinal bowel distress.

"Well, what did you find?" I asked Dr. Diamond shortly after he was done.

"Based on these X-rays and your fever, your tender abdomen and bloody diarrhea, you may have an inflammatory bowel disease known as Crohn's disease," he replied unemotionally. He might as well have been reading a Dow Jones stock quotation.

"What the heck is Crohn's disease?"

"Well, it's a chronic disease we don't know much about, and at the moment there is no known cure."

No cure! I hardly heard anything else he said as my mind struggled to imagine no longer kicking for the Chargers or what living with this disease would be like for the rest of my life.

That night, still in shock, I relayed Dr. Diamond's diagnosis to Dad.

"Well, now we know," he said, "and it'll be easier to figure out what we're fighting. I really don't know much about Crohn's disease, Rolfie. Let's go see if we can find out more about it."

That was easier said than done back then. Today, we would whip out an iPhone, do a quick online search, and receive a fire hose of information about Crohn's disease. But in 1978, Dad led me into his study, which was lined with hundreds of medical books. He pulled a few from the shelf, gave me a couple, and then set the rest down on his desk. We began poring over the volumes, but it didn't take Dad long to find what he was looking for.

What he discovered was not very comforting.

LEARNING CURVE

According to Dad's medical texts, Crohn's disease can affect any portion of the digestive tract, but it typically affects the small intestine and/or the colon. Symptoms can include vomiting, fever, night sweats, loss of appetite, general feelings of weakness, severe abdominal cramps, abdominal pain, and diarrhea (often bloody). Weight loss is common. Cause: unknown.

Clearly, most of those symptoms fit me. I couldn't believe what I was reading. My face flushed, and sweat began to form on my upper lip.

Is This How Crohn's Disease Is Treated Today?

I just described the standard treatment for Crohn's disease in the late 1970s—when there wasn't much known about the disease—was the prescription of prednisone and azulfidine. You may be wondering: *Is that what my doctor would say today?*

Prednisone and azulfidine may still be prescribed today, although your doctor now has many other options available and may propose newer drugs like Dipentum, Colazide, Asacol, Lialda, and Pentasa. These drugs are classified as immunosuppressants, meaning they stop the immune system from causing inflammation. The goal of prescribing immunosuppressants for those symptomatic with Crohn's disease is to get the disease under control and to avoid surgery.

Another powerful weapon in modern medicine's arsenal to treating Crohn's disease today is the use of biologic drugs like Humira, Remicade, or Cimzia. Biologics are antibodies that target particular proteins and cells in order to block inflammation in the gut and are administered by infusion.

Dad, meanwhile, became engrossed in his medical books. He had his researcher's hat on.

"It says here that some people go through a bout with Crohn's, but that it sometimes goes into remission forever, or at least for long periods of time," said Dad encouragingly. "But at the other end of the spectrum, it says surgery or multiple surgeries may be necessary, sometimes requiring the patient to end up with an ostomy."

"What's an ostomy, Dad?"

When my father outlined the procedure, I thought he was describing a fate worse than death.

Dad saw the distressed look on my face. "Let's not jump to conclusions," he reminded me. "We don't know yet for sure that this is what you have."

At my next visit, Dr. Diamond drew more blood and started me on the standard treatment for Crohn's disease. He prescribed prednisone (a powerful anti-inflammatory and immunosuppressant corticosteroid drug) and azulfidine (an anti-bacterial drug) to reduce the symptoms. He told me that I could also expect another test—the dreaded colonoscopy.

"A colonoscopy is a way for the doctor to perform a visual exam of the lining of your colon and look for inflammation, polyps, or ulcerations," Dr. Diamond explained. "The procedure will also allow us to take a small biopsy of the lining of the colon, which will help in making a good diagnosis."

To me at that time, the thought of someone inserting a long steel object up my rectum sounded terribly painful and about the most humiliating medical test a human being could be asked to endure.

I was right. When I returned for the procedure a few days later, I was told to put on a gown and lie on the examining table face down. My gown wasn't tied, leaving my backside open for the whole world to see. Just then, a nurse walked into the room.

"So, this is what a pro football player looks like," she said, trying to be funny. I was in no mood for humor and gritted my teeth until I was given mild anesthesia.

Although I couldn't feel much, I had a vague sensation that I was being "plumbed" by an invasive device traveling way too far up my rectum. Let's just say the scoping procedure was not meant to build anybody's self-esteem.

Afterward, I asked Dr. Diamond two questions that had been gnawing at me: "What is the prognosis, and will I still be able to play football?"

He hesitated for a minute. "The disease impacts people differently, but I don't see any reason why you can't continue to play, at least for the time being," he answered. "We'll just see how it goes."

As I left and gingerly walked to the parking lot with my mom, I didn't say much. As she drove me home, my thoughts were racing. I feared this illness and what it might mean for my future. I feared more tests and possible surgery. I feared telling the Chargers that I was sick and worried that the coaches might not want to take any chances and release me so they could bring in a healthy kicker.

I had no idea how this was going to all play out, but I also knew there was nothing more I could do except see if the treatments the doctor was prescribing would begin to work . . . and take it one day at a time.

The uncertainty was incredibly difficult.

No Guarantees

The sobering reality about pro football is that you live from game to game. Contrary to what most people think, the vast majority of NFL contracts are *not* guaranteed. That means that if your performance level drops off, the team has the right to cut you in a heartbeat and not be obligated to pay the rest of your contract. It happens all the time.

The Chargers fell into a tailspin after the Holy Roller loss, and Coach Prothro "resigned" when the club was 1-3. Don Coryell, who had tried to recruit me to play at San Diego State, was named the new coach. I soon discovered that Coach Coryell, with his sharp nose, piercing eyes, and excitable lisp, was an *intense* guy. But he was also an inspirational coach who brought out the best in his players. We all developed an instant liking for him and his infectious enthusiasm.

Back in college, there were lots of things to take our minds off football. If it wasn't classes, homework, or exams, there was always some campus activity going on. In the pros, Coryell reminded us, we were expected to concentrate on football six days a week. As for himself, he took *no* days off, often sleeping at the stadium while preparing for games. Even when he was at home, his mind never strayed very far from football.

To illustrate this point, one morning Coach Coryell's wife asked him to take the garbage down to the street on trash pick-up day. The Coryells' house was at the top of a long driveway, so to save time,

Coach would often put the trash bags in his trunk, drive them down to the curb, and drop them before heading off to work. On this particular day, he tossed the smelly bags into the back of his car, but by the time he reached the street, his mind had already started thinking about our next opponent. He drove straight to the stadium, blissfully unaware that he had forgotten to leave the trash out at the curb.

Unfortunately, this was one of those weeks where Coach and his staff worked late into the night, and he decided to sleep over at the stadium. The next afternoon, a security guard walking by Coach Coryell's car smelled a powerful odor. He alerted Coryell that there was a funny smell coming from the back of his car—and then Coach realized what he had done. Well, the story made the rounds in the locker room, and we all had a good laugh about it . . . including Coach.

Practice was never dull with Coach Coryell prowling the field, but he didn't mess with the kickers. He generally let our punter and me do our own thing and trusted us to be ready at game time.

The way I liked to prepare for Sunday's game was to kick hard on Wednesdays and Thursdays, taper off on Fridays with just a handful of kicks, and not kick at all on Saturdays. By the time game day rolled around on Sunday, my leg had a lot of pop, and I was ready to go.

Saturdays were always one of the fun days of the week for the players, especially us kickers. If we were playing at home, we'd have an early meeting and then a walk-through practice in the stadium. While the offense and defense went through their game plan, the punter, Jeff West, and I would get some exercise by playing catch and running imaginary pass patterns on the stadium field. The fun exercise helped burn off some nervous energy that was already building up for Game Day and gave us a good stretch.

If we had an away game, we would have our short Saturday practice in our stadium, and then the players would hurry off to a nearby deli or taco shop to grab something to eat before boarding the team buses for the airport. By the time the chartered 727 lifted off from Lindbergh Field, however, it was no longer fun and games. This was a business trip, and the players settled into their own routine as they prepared for the upcoming battle.

When I started feeling ill, the fun Saturday morning walk-throughs turned into something to be endured instead of enjoyed. Any running or quick movements brought sharp pain to my abdomen, and I found it difficult to play catch or run pass patterns. I was hurting constantly and no longer felt like laughing or socializing much with the guys.

As an athlete who knew his body like an Indy mechanic knows his race car, I felt myself changing. I began to lose weight. My leg began to lose its strength and pop, and my kicks didn't carry like they used to. Dr. Diamond told me that while the medications helped manage my inflammation, they also broke down muscle protein, so I had to be careful not to work out too hard. Trying to balance all that and remain in top physical condition was becoming nearly impossible and weighed heavily on my mind.

COMPLAINT CITY

Amazingly, if you looked at my statistics, I was still performing well and having a great season. I knew, however, that my good form was a bit of an illusion because I was relying more and more on timing and technique to get me through each Sunday. I feared the afternoon when I would be called upon to kick a long field goal and wouldn't have the leg strength to reach the goalposts.

I confided my doubts to punter Jeff West, my roommate on the road, and Wayne Sevier, our special teams coach. But the only people who really knew everything about my situation were my parents.

I was eating more and more often at my folks because I couldn't find the energy to prepare meals myself. Just the thought of cooking made me nauseous. At home, Mom and Dad could see the changes in me. They were also on the receiving end of my grouchiness and complaints, which were starting to come more frequently.

"I don't know what's going on," I grumbled one evening. "It's been six weeks, and I'm still not feeling well. Why aren't I getting any better? This Dr. Diamond doesn't know my @#$ from a hole in the ground. Are you really sure he knows what he's doing, Dad?" I was really frustrated.

Dad didn't know how to respond, but he was upset and frustrated for a different reason. He had spent his entire life studying medicine, and now he felt like he wasn't even able to help his own son or clearly explain what was happening to me. After listening to another twenty minutes of me feeling sorry for myself, he had had enough.

"Quit bitching and fight harder to get better," he said sharply. "Take control of this. Maybe you should get out of this stupid football anyway. Get a real job. Then maybe you can get away from the stress of all this."

His comments really hurt me.

"Dad, this isn't caused by stress!" I yelled back. "Everything we read says it isn't, and you know that. If I stop playing football, what am I going to do? There's no guarantee this disease will go away, and then I'm just sick without a job! I'm fighting as best I can. I'm doing everything I can. Do you think I *like* being sick?"

I was so hurt and so angry and so scared that I stormed out of the dining room and ran up to my old bedroom. Mom came up ten minutes later, as she often would after a disagreement in the family. She found me lying on my bed, curled up in a fetal position, trying to stifle my sobs. The pain was so bad, and the reality of where I found myself was overwhelming. I was at the end of my rope.

"Are you okay, Rolf?" Mom asked, gently stroking my forehead. "You know Dad didn't mean what he said. He's just worried, too. He doesn't know how to handle this, and we both wish there was something we could do for you. You know how Dad is. He feels things so deeply, but he sometimes doesn't know how to express his own emotions."

"Mom, it's not fair for him to say that. Doesn't he know I hate being sick and that I'm doing everything I can to fight this thing? I'd do anything to get rid of it."

"I know," Mom said. "It's hard on all of us, especially seeing you in so much pain and not being able to do anything about it. But I want you to know how much we love you. Let's all just keep doing our best and see where it takes us."

Mom gave me a gentle hug and wouldn't let go until my sobs began to subside.

Getting Nowhere

Each time I tried to get some specific information from Dr. Diamond, he seemed to evade me.

In my frustration, I decided to seek out other medical advice. I felt like I needed to do something more . . . maybe change my diet, try some alternate kinds of treatments, or find a doctor with a stronger, more confident personality. Someone who was really up on the latest research, knew everything there was to know about inflammatory bowel disease, and who could encourage me through this very rough time.

My life was at a major crossroads. Should I continue to suck it up and play in pain—or stop? Would continuing to kick put my life at risk? Was playing football part of the problem? I also wondered if my promising young football career was about to come to a sudden end . . . and that scared me. Life seemed so hard and so unfair. I just wasn't sure what to do.

When I described my frustrations about my doctor to Dad, he reminded me that Dr. Diamond was the head of the gastroenterology department at UC San Diego and had a good reputation. Nevertheless, Dad was beginning to have some misgivings as well.

Meanwhile, my weakening condition was becoming more apparent to the Chargers—and to the public. I knew I needed to sit down with Coach Coryell and explain what was really going on with me, so I stopped in to see him after team meetings one day.

"Coach, we have a chance to make the playoffs," I started, "and I've got to tell you that I'm struggling out there. If it ever comes down to the team needing a long field goal to win, I'm not sure I'll be able to do the job for you."

Coryell got up from behind his desk and walked over to where I was standing.

"Rolf, we've really come to depend on you, and there is nobody I'd rather have out there than you. How about if we have somebody else kick off and see if we can help you get through the rest of the season that way? You tell me how much you want to practice—or if you don't. Whatever you say is fine with me."

I was blown away by his support. I thanked him and vowed to do whatever I could to get through the last few games.

When I stopped kicking off, the media knew something was going on. There had been speculation that something was physically wrong with me, so I let the truth come out. Readers of the *San Diego Union* and the *Evening Tribune* learned that I was suffering from Crohn's disease, an inflammation of the intestinal tract that was poorly understood by the medical community and had no known cure.

The newspaper articles prompted letters from well-meaning people who suggested various treatments that had worked for them: eat more roughage, lay off dairy products, add zinc to my diet, mix bran with every meal, practice hypnosis, and consider acupuncture. Some suggestions were bizarre: One person thought I should lock myself in a hotel room and watch *Laurel and Hardy* films and laugh until the disease went away.

I appreciated the support from the fans, but I also felt like I had tried everything. I had started meeting with a nutritionist, looking for any dietary help to keep my weight and strength up. I had also made my first contact with the Crohn's & Colitis Foundation of America, figuring it couldn't hurt to hear what they had to say.

The last month of the 1978 season was especially difficult. My health was deteriorating so quickly that after kicking on Sundays, the doctors decided to check me into a local hospital for treatment. In order to give my bowels a rest and ensure I was getting enough nutrition, I would be hooked up to an intravenous feeding line inserted into the jugular vein in my neck for the entire week. Doctors forbade me to eat anything, hoping that would allow my inflamed intestines to heal. I would then be released on Saturday to spend the night in the Chargers team hotel and play the game on Sunday. After the game I would return to the hospital, where the feeding line was re-inserted and I would repeat the process.

The weird thing is that I continued to kick well, so the Chargers wanted me to keep playing. At one point, I hit sixteen consecutive field goals, and the team was really coming together. Although we had lost too many games early in the season to earn a spot in the playoffs, we were making life miserable for a bunch of other teams trying to get to the postseason.

Our last game of the 1978 season pitted us against the Houston Oilers. They were one of the best teams in the NFL with their star running back, Earl Campbell, and folksy coach, Bum Phillips. An hour before the game, the pain in my gut was so bad that I couldn't even zip up my football pants.

That afternoon in the Astrodome, quarterback Dan Fouts was sensational and piloted "Air Coryell" to perfection. We went out and crushed the Oilers, but that meant a long day at the office for me. I had to kick six extra points and a field goal, experiencing excruciating pain each time I jogged onto the field. I couldn't wait for the game to be over.

As for the Chargers, we finished the season by really coming together. Our 9-7 record didn't qualify us for the playoffs, but with Fouts in complete command of the new passing system and Coryell and his coaching staff establishing one of the most innovative offenses in the league, the Chargers believed 1979 could be their year.

But as bright as the Chargers' future appeared to be, my future was increasingly uncertain. I, too, wondered what 1979 had in store . . . but I wasn't sure I would even be around to find out.

5

SLOWLY SINKING

CHARGERS TRAINING CAMP
JULY 1979

When I reported to the Chargers training camp at UC San Diego, ready to start my third season with the team, my ongoing medical problems arrived with me. All through the spring and summer, Dr. Diamond and his medical team had tried to stabilize my Crohn's disease so I could continue to play. I had worked on changing my diet, tried traditional treatments and several alternate kinds of therapy, including visiting an acupuncturist, and trained as hard as my body would allow to regain my strength.

I convinced myself I was getting better. I had gained some weight, but I was still experiencing piercing cramps and frustrating diarrhea at times. At this point, I didn't know what else to do . . . so I kept my head down and entered camp ready to compete for my job.

When we started the traditional two-a-day workouts, I quickly shed the pounds I had worked so hard to put on during the off-season. To make matters worse, I didn't have much of an appetite and was having a hard time eating, unlike my teammates. Three times a day, I watched these mammoth athletes devour everything in sight at the buffet line, going back two or three times at each sitting. As for me, I was lucky if I could keep down two pieces of dry toast and a banana.

Since it was obvious I wasn't 100 percent, the Chargers team doctors and athletic trainers were brought back into the picture. They struggled to treat me, too, but were willing to try anything to help. To compensate for my poor appetite, they came up with a plan: I would drink special high-caloric "milkshakes," brimming with amino acids and carbohydrates that they would prepare before and after each practice in the training room. I appreciated their efforts and forced down these less-than-great-tasting shakes as best I could.

When I braved regular food at the training table, intense cramps would continue to attack me, and the diarrhea worsened. I always had to know where I could quickly find a bathroom and wondered again how long I could keep this up. When the Chargers broke camp at the end of August, the team doctors and nutritionists decided to cut out solid food altogether and put me on a strict high-caloric, amino-acid drink diet.

In order to take in enough calories to maintain my weight, I had to drink *fifteen* of these vile purple-colored concoctions each day. Since I was spending much of my free time at home with my parents, Mom learned to make the drinks in the family blender. The taste, however, was so bad that I had to literally squeeze my nose when I drank one. If I didn't, I would gag and the contents would come right back up.

I was one sick puppy when the 1979 NFL season finally opened . . . but I had regained my job.

LATE HIT

Like the year before, the season began in Seattle, and once again I kicked four field goals in a big Chargers victory. The team was good . . . really good . . . and we were preseason picks to go deep in the playoffs. I wanted to be a part of it. Unfortunately, things were different for me now. After each field goal, I would return to the bench in excruciating pain, feeling as if someone was turning a knife stuck into my abdomen.

In the jubilant locker room following the game, while my teammates whooped and hollered around me about our big win, I sat in front of my locker with my head buried in a towel, tears running down my cheeks. I knew I couldn't go on much longer like this . . . but I just didn't know what to do. Something had to give.

It happened the next week when the Oakland Raiders came into town. Emotions ran high on both benches, and in the stadium, memories of the "Holy Roller" game were still vivid in everyone's minds.

Late in the first half, we scored our third touchdown of the day, and I ran out to kick the routine PAT. My kick sailed through the goalposts, but as I was following through, I was suddenly run into hard and knocked to the ground. The Raiders' Lester Hayes, a defensive back known for his "in your face" play, had slammed his shoulder into my unprotected ribs on my left side as he was trying to block the kick.

The violent blow sent me flying, knocking the wind out of me and leaving me on the stadium floor, struggling to get a breath. As team physicians and trainers sprinted out to where I was lying flat on my back, I fought hard to breathe and couldn't move. The "roughing the kicker" rules were a lot more lax in those days, and it was determined that Hayes had been blocked into me, so no penalty was called.

After what seemed like ten minutes—but was probably just a couple of minutes—I was gingerly helped off the field, wincing with each breath. A team doctor escorted me to the locker room, where preliminary X-rays were taken. My ribs hurt terribly, and when I couldn't take a deep breath without pain, the doctors feared I might have broken some ribs. Either way, I knew I was finished for the afternoon. I showered, was handed an ice bag for my ribs, and returned to the sidelines to watch the rest of the game. After the Chargers won, a team doctor drove me to the hospital for more X-rays. The results: three cracked ribs on my left side.

Supported with a belly wrap that seemed to do absolutely no good, I spent the early part of the week recovering at my parents' home. I would go to the stadium for treatment and attend team meetings, but practicing was out of the question.

One morning late in the week, on my drive to the stadium, I was listening to a sports report on the radio when I heard the announcer say that he would be returning in just a moment for a special interview with Coach Coryell.

I turned up the volume.

"Your kicker, Rolf Benirschke, was injured last week and didn't return for the second half," the sports guy began. "What's his condition, and do you believe he will be able to play on Sunday?"

"Rolf's a tough guy," replied Coryell in his now familiar lisp. "There's no problem. We need him, and we expect him back this Sunday."

I nearly drove off the road. *Holy cow, what am I going to do?* I could hardly get out of bed without pain, and the thought of trying to kick seemed impossible.

I played.

STILL KICKING

The pressure to be on the field was constant. We all felt it, and I felt it perhaps more than others. Since Dean Meier's first letter back in my rookie season, I had converted 34 of my last 38 kicks. Despite my health problems, I was still enjoying the challenge of producing in the clutch, and I loved being part of a team on the rise.

The media was writing complimentary stories about me, and I had become an integral part of the Chargers' success. Three weeks into the season, we were undefeated and one of the league's marquee teams.

Week 4 sent us to Boston to play the New England Patriots. My injured ribs kept me from practicing, and I was only able to kick in games because the doctors injected me with Novocain. Not being able to practice was affecting my timing, and I suddenly found myself really struggling. During pregame warm-ups, I could barely kick a 35-yard field goal with a stiff wind at my back. To make matters more frustrating, New England kicker John Smith—kicking toward the same goalpost—was air-mailing 50-yarders high into the net. And Smith wasn't known for having a strong leg. I was totally demoralized and scared I wouldn't be able to deliver if we needed a long kick.

The Patriots won the coin toss, elected to take the wind, and put three touchdowns on the scoreboard in the first quarter. We never recovered and lost 27-21.

I couldn't wait to board the team plane for the long, cross-country flight home. As I settled into my seat, the difficult reality of my situation weighed heavily on my mind. I was conflicted. I wanted to play, loved to play, and had hoped that the treatments would begin working and that my illness would go into remission. But I hadn't improved. Now I knew something had to be done and that I needed to tell the coaches I really couldn't kick any more. I felt like I had become a liability. My illness had worsened, and it was clear I was putting our team in jeopardy.

Not long after the team jet took off, I felt feverish, and pain assaulted my abdomen once again. I was exhausted. *Perhaps if I sleep, I'll wake up and this nightmare will be over.* But after dozing for about an hour, I was jolted awake by another wave of intense cramps. I knew what they meant, so I hurried back to the lavatory, sat down, and relieved myself.

As I returned to my seat, my world suddenly started spinning and turned black. I slowly collapsed in the aisle. Teammates scrambled to lay me flat and called for the team doctors and trainers. They quickly made me as comfortable as possible, but I was on fire. My temperature was 103 degrees, yet my body was shaking with chills. The team doctor quickly ordered my teammates to carefully lay me across three seats and wrap me in several blankets as they tried to figure out what to do next.

When the chartered jet touched down at Lindbergh Field, I felt a little better and had regained some energy. A Chargers official had asked the pilot to get a message to my parents to meet me at the airport, and they were at the gate when the team plane landed. I convinced them that I didn't need to go to the hospital but agreed to go home with them.

In my heart, I knew I probably should have been hospitalized, but I hoped this would pass, just like all the other times. Besides, I was scared and still hadn't settled on what to do. I thought that once I was taken to the hospital, there would be no turning back and my season would definitely be over.

All night and into the early morning hours, I tossed and turned in my bed. The pain in my gut felt like someone was sticking me with a hot poker, and my fever had returned. I regretted talking Mom and Dad out of a trip to the hospital. I felt terrible, and my spirits were as low as ever.

When Mom came in to check on me in the morning, the soaking-wet sheets immediately told her the fever had broken, but I was weak and worn out. Mom helped me out of bed and realized I needed to see the doctor right away. After a meager breakfast, she drove me to Dr. Diamond's office.

Before I left, I called Coach Coryell and told him I would have to miss the noon team meeting but would report back to him after seeing the doctor.

At the doctor's office, Dr. Diamond listened to the latest episode on the plane. He had me step on a scale, poked and prodded me a bit, and then shook his head.

"Rolf, we've tried everything. We've tried medications, we've tried diet, and we've tried rest. The medications don't seem to be working, and things are getting worse. I don't know how you've been able to play as long as you have, but you're really sick. We have run out of options, and your life is in danger. I really believe you need surgery. There just isn't anything more we can do medically. I'm going to call the surgeon to see when he can get you in. I'm sorry."

Surgery! Did he know what he was saying? Did Dr. Diamond realize that undergoing surgery would remove me from my teammates, end my season, and perhaps my career? Yet he mentioned surgery so casually. Didn't he know how *huge* this decision was?

As I slowly processed what Dr. Diamond was saying, I knew he was right. A measure of relief fell over me. I realized I was at the end of the line and something needed to be done. There were clearly no other options. In a sense, I was relieved to have the decision made for me before I cost the team a victory.

On the way back from the doctor's office, I asked Mom to stop by San Diego Stadium, where the team practiced and where the Chargers offices were. I needed to break the news to Coach Coryell so he could start looking for another kicker. He had been so good to me during this ordeal, and now I had to tell him I couldn't kick anymore. I felt like I was letting him down, and that killed me. When I walked into Coach's office, he was a little surprised to see me, but he could tell by the look on my face that something was up.

"Coach," I began, trying to hold back the tears, "the doctor says I need surgery and that I won't be able to play again this season."

As I expected, Coryell was more concerned about me than his football team.

"Don't worry about us, Rolf. We'll find another kicker," he said, shaking his head sadly. "You do what you have to do and get well as soon as you can. I'll let the rest of the team know at meetings later today."

"Thanks, Coach."

"Good luck and know that we'll all be pulling for you," he said while shaking my hand.

I turned away quickly so he couldn't see the tears beginning to stream down my cheeks. Then I quietly slipped out of his office.

As Mom and I drove out of the stadium parking lot, a thousand thoughts flooded my mind. I wondered if I had put on my Chargers uniform for the last time, if I had been in my last locker room, kicked my last field goal, and was leaving my teammates for the last time. But lurking deeper were thoughts of the upcoming surgery.

Would I survive? Would I ever be healthy again?

Suddenly, those became the bigger questions.

UNIVERSITY HOSPITAL
TUESDAY, OCTOBER 2

I had put off the inevitable long enough. One year of debilitating diarrhea and constant abdominal pain had taken its toll. I was worn out; I couldn't take it anymore. I had exhausted my reserves. I was ready to submit myself to whatever medical solutions the doctors presented to me. I was done.

As I sat at the nurse's admitting station, squeezing my hands tightly together, anxiety oozed out of every pore of my body. I was scared . . . really scared.

When my head strayed a bit too far to the right, my eyes met Mom's. Emotions suddenly welled up inside of me, and I started to tear up. "Mom, can you believe this is happening?"

At this point, the seasoned hospital admitting clerk recognized the delicate situation. "We don't have to finish this work-up now," she said sympathetically. "We can complete it later."

She smiled and turned to the orderly standing at the door. "Carlos, you can take Mr. Benirschke up to his room, 11 West."

As we left the office and headed toward the elevator, another shot of intense pain tore at my insides. I paused and closed my eyes tightly—as though that might help ease the pain—and felt Mom squeeze my arm gently.

"We're doing the right thing, Rolf," she whispered. "We're doing the right thing."

After getting settled in my room, Dr. Diamond, the surgeon, and several other residents and medical students came in to poke and prod me one last time. They determined that I needed surgery, but they thought I needed to build up my weight and strength for a couple of weeks before they could operate. To do that, they were going to keep me in the hospital and put me on TPN—total parenteral nutrition.

I learned that TPN involved putting a central IV line into the jugular or subclavian vein in my neck. Large amounts of fats, concentrated dextrose, amino acids, and other essential minerals would be administered around the clock through the IV to provide all of my nutrition. I would eat no food.

Dr. Gerald Peskin would be the lead surgeon, and once the reins were handed over to him, I saw or heard little from Dr. Diamond. It was as though he disappeared from the medical team. I sensed he was embarrassed that he hadn't taken more control of the situation and that our relationship wasn't the best. In fairness, though, there might not have been much more that Dr. Diamond could have done, and I certainly wasn't an easy case with the pressure we both felt trying to keep me on the field.

Either way, I was happy to have Dr. Peskin now leading the medical team. He was easy to talk to and instilled great confidence in my parents and me. In getting me ready for the procedure, he explained that he would make a mid-line incision on my abdomen from just below my sternum to my pubic bone and resect—cut out—the diseased part of the bowel and stitch me back up.

"Once the incision heals, you should be able to function very nicely with only a small part of your intestine missing," Dr. Peskin said. "In fact, I think you'll even play football again." That made me smile, but playing football again seemed a long ways away.

Getting the huge IV needle into my jugular vein was not fun. I was asked to lie on my back and hang my head over the end of the bed so the nurse could expose the large vein. It was uncomfortable, and when she missed the vein on her first attempt, blood spurted everywhere.

"Don't worry. This disease has been a pain in the neck since day one," I murmured with grim humor, trying to ease her obvious embarrassment. But I was in so much discomfort that I didn't care about the details. I just wanted to get this over with.

University Hospital
Thursday, October 4

The west wing of University Hospital's eleventh floor was reserved for VIPs. Rooms were a little bigger and decorated with a little more flair. The food, served on fine china, was supposed to be better. Perhaps this was the floor where hospital authorities thought the younger son of Dr. Kurt Benirschke, head of UCSD's Pathology department, should go. Or perhaps they sent me to the eleventh floor because I was a San Diego Charger.

Unfortunately, the eleventh floor was not really set up for critical cases; the sixth floor was.

Down on the sixth floor, registered nurse Colleen Holt was talking with Bertha Robles, the floor's nursing supervisor, about the hospital's new celebrity patient.

"Why would they put him on 11?" Colleen asked, "He should be one of *our* patients. All the IBD cases are here. We're the ones most qualified to take care of him."

"You're absolutely right," Bertha responded. "He really should be here with us."

Colleen called the ward clerk, who called Dr. Peskin, and the matter was resolved. I'd be transferred to the sixth floor the next day. That turned out to be a good thing.

For the rest of the day, however, I stayed on the eleventh floor, where the TPN hyperalimentation entered my body at 40 cc per hour. Everything was going according to plan.

Mom continued to comfort me, and Dad stopped by three times. He didn't have to travel far; he worked in the Pathology lab on the second floor.

"How are you, Rolfie?" Dad always spoke with an upbeat voice each time he came in, but I could hear his concern.

I could hardly look him in the eyes. I didn't want to cry in front of my father. For one of the few times in my life, I recognized that no matter how much Dad knew about medicine, he couldn't control the situation in which we found ourselves. That had to be difficult for him, especially since he had devoted his life to scientific research and the medical field.

"Just a few more days . . . you've got to hang in there, Rolf," he said in his soft German accent. I could feel the resolution in his voice, born of a man who had overcome so much and achieved everything he put his mind to. He bent over and gently touched my shoulder. "We'll get through this. I promise!"

"Why do I feel I can't?" I pleaded, turning my head away. "I feel so absolutely helpless . . . so out of control. I'm worried about what's going to happen with my life, with football. I'm scared about the surgery. I'm worried that maybe . . . ."

I couldn't bring myself to finish the sentence. The unthinkable—dying—was unsayable.

Dad thought for a minute. "I know, Rolfie. We've got to take this one day at a time. We'll find a way to get through this. Don't worry about football. It's just a game, something you do for now, but not forever. Who's to say the stress of football didn't cause all this to happen?"

I turned my head to the window, suddenly angry. "C'mon, Dad. We both read the same books, the same articles. The research says that stress is *not* the cause of this."

It was an old, familiar argument between Dad and me . . . and now it was starting up again. For years, Dad had reminded all of us children that sports were a pastime, something to be enjoyed but not to be taken too seriously. Skiing and tennis made sense, he said, because they were recreational sports. "You could do those things on the weekends for the rest of your life, but the week was meant for work," he'd say. "Playing football is not working!"

In my hospital room, Dad decided not to reopen the argument, but his comment about stress causing my health problems hung in the air.

Mom rose from her chair. "Kurt, you're only upsetting him. He doesn't need that right now."

"I suppose you're right, Marion."

Dad got up from the edge of the bed. "I have to leave for New York tomorrow to give a speech at Cornell University. I'll be back Sunday night. I'm sorry if I upset you. That was not my intention. I want so much for the pain to be gone for you . . . for you to find peace. Believe me, Rolf."

"I know, Dad, I know. But please understand that football and sports are important to me."

Later, when I was alone, I tried to drink some water. That was all I was allowed to take orally, and even a simple glass of water didn't sit well in my stomach. I was still grimacing when Dr. Peskin breezed into my room with two nurses on his heels.

"How's my football hero doing?" he asked cheerfully.

"Lousy, really lousy," I answered, forcing a wry smile.

Despite my poor attitude, I liked Dr. Peskin's genial manner. *At least he looks me in the eye and asks how I'm doing, a refreshing change.*

"The good news is that we're going to move you down to the sixth floor tomorrow. Not that you aren't getting good care up here, but it'll be better on 6."

I thanked him. When Dr. Peskin left, he stopped at the nurses' station and wrote the following note on my chart: "Dx of Crohn's disease of the terminal ileum, ascending and transverse colon. Admitted for HAL, then planned resection of involved segment of the bowel. Also has oropharyngeal candidiasis for past two weeks."

Oropharyngeal candidiasis is a yeast infection of the mouth and throat, relatively common in people taking prednisone regularly but frustrating nonetheless. Prednisone is a wonder drug when it comes to reducing inflammation, but it has a legion of side effects, of which yeast infections might be the least serious.

Another side effect of prednisone is that it causes the body to retain water. On the morning of my second day at University Hospital, I weighed more than 150 pounds, down from my healthy weight of 184, but up from my admitting weight of 145 pounds. I felt a bit like the Michelin man . . . all pumped up.

Dr. Peskin visited me the following morning, a Friday. He had looked at my latest blood draw and didn't like what he had seen, so when he left, he ordered two units of blood by transfusion. In addition, he increased the hyperal solution intake to 50 cc per hour.

Peskin was also disturbed by my increasing lack of motivation and feelings of depression. He arranged for hospital psychologist Dr. Harvey Ward to visit me after I was transferred down from the eleventh floor.

At one o'clock that afternoon, I was taken by wheelchair to the sixth floor. Nurses Colleen Holt and Bertha Robles greeted me at the elevator and escorted me to Room 9. I was agitated, and my eyes darted everywhere. I didn't engage much in conversation and couldn't wait for them to leave my new room.

Later, over a cup of coffee, the two nurses discussed their new patient.

"It's been a long time since we've seen anybody that frightened," Colleen remarked.

"Terrible," Bertha agreed. "His eyes are almost scary. They're so full of fear."

Dr. Ward, the hospital psychologist, came to my room and discovered a patient who wanted nothing to do with him. I was moody and uncommunicative.

"How come you have all this built-up hostility?" he probed.

I didn't answer.

"Rolf, tell me what's bothering you."

I couldn't believe he was asking me these ridiculous questions and remained uncooperative. Just then, thankfully, my parents walked into my room. They were on the way to the airport, where Dad would fly to New York for his speech. Two friends also appeared within moments.

They sat in the back of the room and listened to Dr. Ward's questioning. I had finally had enough and spoke to him, but more out of politeness because of the guests in the room.

"Please leave us alone," I said. "Please leave *me* alone. I'm not up for this right now."

The psychologist left and wrote the following on my chart: "Severely depressed. Fortunately, patient has a substantial social support system."

That afternoon, my hyperal intake was increased, and my prednisone dosage was doubled as life in the hospital room settled into a routine. I dozed off a lot, waking up only when nurses and interns came around. Time crawled slowly.

I had to undergo two exams—another upper GI and a proctoscope. The barium swallow, as expected, was merely awful. The proctoscope was humiliating.

Meanwhile, I met a new nurse, Helen Delgado, who worked the 2 p.m. to 10 p.m. shift. She was a special woman full of kindness and compassion, but also capable of speaking directly to me when necessary.

The first evening, after listening to my "woe is me" litany, she scolded my attitude. "It's not the end of the world, you know. Stop acting as if you think it is."

The rebuke stung, but it got me thinking. *Maybe she's right.* I opened up to her, something I hadn't done with Dr. Ward.

"It seems like I've been fighting this for so long, though. I just don't have anything left."

"What you've got to do is start trusting, start accepting a little help from all of us," she said. "We're here to support you. You've got to believe that."

Helen brought me crackers, the first solid food permitted by my doctors. Shortly after eating one, however, my intestines started to cramp, and the crescendo of pain I had become so used to returned once again. I tried to put the crackers on my nightstand, but they fell to the linoleum floor. Helen picked them up and patted my arm.

"You tried. It didn't work, and that's okay. Forget it."

SATURDAY, OCTOBER 6

11 A.M.

University Hospital is associated with UCSD, and as such, was a teaching hospital. That meant a steady stream of residents, interns, and medical students flowed in and out of my room. The exams and discussions were never ending.

That morning, a swarm of interns invaded the premises, led by primary intern Cammy Mowery. Normally, I at least tried to smile at my visitors and act somewhat civil. But this morning I was in more pain that usual and was distant and rude, plainly not happy with another intrusion.

After the group had left, Dr. Mowery returned to my room for a visit and the chance to get to know me a little better. She talked about my upcoming surgery and asked about any fears I had. I appreciated that and confided, "Sometimes I think I'm *not* going to get out of here." I teared up, feeling sorry for myself.

"You want to know the truth?" Dr. Mowery asked. She didn't wait for an answer. "The truth is you're not the first to go through this. We have half a dozen other people on the floor with inflammatory bowel disorders, and across the nation, there are hundreds—make that thousands—of other people in hospitals with exactly the same thing you have. The point is, you're not that unusual. And knowing a little bit about your background in football, I have confidence you can get through this."

I chewed on that one for a while.

Dr. Peskin walked in a short time later with good news. The proctoscope and upper GI showed nothing unexpected.

"Now, I want to do an IVP," he said.

I knew what an IVP was. "Are you doing this to see if I have kidney stones?" I had undergone an intravenous pyelogram in college when I needed a painful kidney stone removed.

"No, what we're really doing is locating your ureters, which extend from your kidneys to your bladder, so we don't accidentally snip them when we open up your abdomen."

I stared at Dr. Peskin. "So there's no chance of avoiding surgery?"

"Almost none," he replied. "We've scheduled your resection surgery for a week from Monday, October 15."

SUNDAY, OCTOBER 7
10 P.M.

Out-of-bed activity is important for anyone confined to extended bed rest because moving around is good for the body in general and helps keep the lungs from collecting fluid, which can lead to pneumonia.

Any movements for me, however, triggered painful consequences. But my nurses had other ideas; they insisted that I walk around.

I preferred to remain quiet in bed and distract myself with whatever was on television, like watching the Chargers play the Broncos in Denver. It was a frustrating game to watch from my hospital bed. We lost 7-0 as my replacement, Roy Gerela, missed three field goals inside 35 yards.

After the game, I turned on the radio and listened to the Chargers' post-game call-in show. I wasn't prepared for what I heard.

"What this team needs is a placekicker," one upset fan stated.

"Gerela stinks! When is Benirschke coming back?" another asked.

"This Gerela fellow is going to really cost us," chimed in another caller. "Even a sick Rolf wouldn't have missed those kicks."

At first, the comments made me feel good that I was missed, but the longer I listened, the more it hurt to hear the anger expressed toward a fellow kicker, a guy who was trying his hardest. Gerela, who had kicked for years with the Super Bowl champion Pittsburgh Steelers, had been a good kicker his whole career.

I couldn't take it any longer. In frustration, I picked up the phone and called the station. They put me on the air immediately.

"This is Rolf Benirschke," I said to the startled host. "I just want to put in a word for Roy Gerela. I know it was a difficult game today, but he's doing the best he can. You can't imagine what he's going through. The grass turf at Mile High Stadium in Denver can be patchy and long, so it's a tough place to kick for anyone, much less a guy who's just getting familiar with a new snapper and holder. So please go easy on Roy, will ya? I promise you there's nobody who wanted to make those kicks more than he did."

Dad returned from New York on Sunday night and stopped by the hospital. He had been away for just a weekend, but in forty-eight hours, he could see pronounced changes in me. I was pale and wan, and the effects of prednisone and hyperalimentation had left me even more bloated around my face, neck, and extremities.

I looked at my father. "It hasn't been a fun day. The Chargers lost in Denver. . . ."

"Never mind," he whispered. "How are you doing?"

"Fine," I replied, but we both knew I was far from that polite response.

The next morning, senior resident Lee Griffith led another group of interns into my room.

Dr. Griffith lifted up my hospital gown and touched my right side, pressing his fingers into my intestines.

"Ouch! That hurts like hell!" I squealed, pushing his hand away. "Do you have to do it so hard?" I was upset.

Ignoring me, the doctor addressed the four interns gathered around my bed. "Did you hear that? The surest sign of intestinal distress."

Glad to be of help.

I received permission to try to eat limited quantities of neutral solid foods, so I chose one of my favorites: pretzels. I took a couple of handfuls and slowly savored the salty taste. Unfortunately, an hour later I was doubling over with cramps, wishing I had never indulged myself.

Dr. Peskin informed me that my kidneys looked good and that I had no stones, but my white blood count was very high: 13,400. (The normal range is 4,000 to 10,000.) A high WBC indicated an infection somewhere.

Then came more jolting news for the Benirschke family. My parents received a phone call from my younger sister, Ingrid, who was living in New York City at the time. Ironically, Ingrid had developed her own set of kidney stones and needed surgery immediately.

The news was very discouraging for my parents.

"What next?" Mom asked Dad sorrowfully.

"Yes, Marion," replied Dad. "What next, indeed?"

When they told me the news, I felt sorry for what my folks must be going through. Now they had two of their children with serious medical problems. The decision was made to fly Ingrid to San Diego and have her join me at University Hospital. The silver lining was that we would be a couple of floors apart, making it easy for my parents to visit us.

That night Ingrid arrived late at Lindbergh Field and surprised me by dropping in and saying hi before heading to my parents' home in La Jolla.

"Hey, big guy," she said as she entered my hospital room. "Are they treating you okay?"

"Ingrid!"

"Isn't this crazy? I almost feel like I'm having sympathy pains," she smiled. Then Ingrid explained why she was in San Diego—to deal with her kidney stones. She told me that she would be admitted to the hospital in the morning.

I could tell by her face that she was shocked by my appearance. I was only fourteen months older than my sister, and we had always been close, united by our common sensitivities and values. After our short visit, Ingrid headed to La Jolla to get some much-needed rest.

On Monday morning, my abdominal cramps returned and were again followed by explosive diarrhea. Another blood work-up was ordered.

The endocrinologist reported: "Patient is getting toxic, although it's unknown if the infection is due to an abscess or to the CVP line."

Since the blood work detected the presence of bacteria in the bloodstream, Dr. Griffith was called in. While he studied my chart, I asked him why I couldn't have the surgery now instead of waiting until next week.

"Understand, we're trying to build up your strength and resistance so you can tolerate the operation better," he reminded me. "But I will address this latest development with Dr. Peskin. If he feels we should operate now, we'll proceed."

The old saying—*Be careful what you ask for, you might just get it*—came to mind. A deep sense of fear shivered through my body.

My eyes darted around the room, and suddenly, I never felt more alone in my life.

6

EARLY CALL

Thursday night was a horror show. My temperature never dropped below 103 degrees, my pulse raced at 150 beats per minute, and my blood pressure was dangerously low.

Early Friday morning, Dr. Peskin felt we couldn't wait six more days for surgery. It was time to take action.

"Rolf," he said. "Wake up."

I opened my eyes and turned my head.

"We're going to move the surgery up to tomorrow. We can't wait any longer."

I thought for a long moment. "Will you have to do an ileostomy?"

An ileostomy was a surgical operation in which the end of the small intestine (the ileum) is brought through the abdomen to the surface of the skin, where an artificial opening—or stoma—is created to divert your fecal waste into a bag that gets attached to your side. As a professional athlete and a single twenty-four-year-old guy, I couldn't imagine living with a bag . . . so ending up with one after surgery was a huge fear for me.

"We don't know yet," replied Dr. Peskin. "We think we just need to do a resection. Your disease appears to be localized to your terminal ileum and part of your colon, but we will see once we are inside."

With a resection, Dr. Peskin would surgically remove the diseased

83

part of my intestines and then sew the two ends of bowel together. This procedure would allow me to dodge the bullet of having to wear an ostomy bag for the rest of my life.

When Dr. Peskin left, Nurse Colleen Holt drew her usual four test tubes of blood from me. By now, my arms were black and blue from the needle sticks, and she was having difficulty finding a vein. Colleen didn't like the way I looked, so she had a student nurse stay with me while she finished her rounds.

A short time later, as Colleen came out of another patient's room, she noticed the call light on for Room 9. Sensing trouble, she ran to my room, where she found me draped over the toilet. The student nurse, who couldn't have weighed more than 105 pounds, was trying to lift me away from the toilet. The odor was awful!

"He had to go," the young nurse explained almost apologetically. "But when he got in here, he got lightheaded and started going to the bathroom standing up. Then he collapsed on the floor. I didn't know what to do."

Colleen ran to the door and called for help. Two other nurses came running, and together the four of them dragged me out of the bathroom.

I had another violent bowel movement about three feet from the bed, soiling the front of Colleen's uniform. The nurses cleaned me up and lifted me into bed as best they could.

With tears of shame in my eyes, I tried to apologize for what happened. "I'm so sorry," I stammered. "I couldn't control myself."

"Don't worry," said Colleen, as she began changing my gown. "It's not the first time, and it certainly won't be the last time for us. Accidents happen."

The nurses took my vital signs. My temperature was a sky-high 104, my pulse had rocketed to 180 beats per minute, and my blood pressure was a shockingly low 80/60. The doctor was called, and my prednisone intake was increased, and antibiotics were added to my IV in preparation.

When my parents got the news of my accident, they came as quickly as they could. I had settled down a little, but my heart rate was still high. I complained about blurry vision.

"My head aches, too, but that's not so bad because it takes my mind off my abdominal pain," I said.

I slowly drifted off to sleep with Mom at my side, gently holding my hand and quietly saying prayers.

Meanwhile, four floors below, my sister, Ingrid, was just coming out of her own surgery. The word was that she was extremely sore but recovering nicely. Mom and Dad asked Nurse Helen Delgado to stay with me while they went downstairs and checked up on Ingrid.

I awoke and smiled at the angel in the white uniform.

"Hi, Helen. Is it morning already?"

"Morning? It's afternoon. You've had a rough day so far, in case you didn't know."

For a week, I had kept the unmentionable deep within, but I had to ask The Question.

"Helen, am I going to die?" I stammered, tears rolling down my cheeks. "Am I going to wake up after the operation, or is this it?"

She nodded with understanding, almost as relieved as I was that the subject had been raised.

"No, Rolf, you're not going to die. And yes, you are going to wake up after your operation."

"It's so awful, Helen. The bad dreams I've been having about not waking up . . . or if I wake up, having a bag around my stomach. A bag! Can you imagine going through life like that? I can't."

"Let's not worry about that now," she soothed. "Let's try to get some rest. You've had a big day and are exhausted."

"I could die, though, right? Something *could* go wrong and that would be it, right?"

"We hope and pray that won't happen. But you need to work at replacing your bad thoughts with good thoughts. It's an act of the will, and it's important to try."

I nodded with understanding. "When's the operation?" I asked.

"It's all set for 8 a.m. tomorrow. I know it's hard to imagine but believe me, you'll feel much better after it's done."

That afternoon, alone in my room, I thought long and hard about my situation. *What happens when you die? Where do you go? Is this all there is?* Ever since I had been hospitalized, I'd been thinking about God and the meaning of life. As if an answer to prayer, Jim Adkins, the youth pastor of the church I was attending, walked into my room.

"Jim, what are you doing here?" I was surprised to see him.

"Well, I've been thinking about you and wanted to come by and let you know everyone at church is praying for you. I know this is a tough time, but perhaps I could take a moment to pray for you and your surgery tomorrow."

Touched by his kindness and the kindness of so many others, tears flowed freely down my cheeks again. I could only answer with a nod of my head. Jim squeezed my hand while he bowed his head and prayed that God would guide the surgeons' hands during the surgery to bring healing to my diseased body.

In the back of the room, my father had slipped in while Jim was praying softly out loud. Although he had never been a churchgoer and had never heard someone pray like that, the emotion and concern he heard in Jim's voice caused him to tear up also. I felt God's presence in that lonely hospital room and knew I was as prepared as I could be for whatever the next day would bring.

The calm did not last long, however. Shortly after Jim left, intern Cammy Mowery came in and began explaining the upcoming surgery to me. Suddenly, I was confronted by the reality of undergoing a major abdominal procedure; I was heading down a road where there was no turning back. When Dr. Mowery held out a pen for me to sign the medical consent forms, she noticed my body tense up when I read that I was giving permission for the doctors to perform an ostomy if they felt it was necessary.

"Cammy, what's the probability of an ostomy?"

"Very low," she replied. "It's routine to include that language in the consent form, just in case."

I signed but still felt terribly uneasy.

FRIDAY, OCTOBER 12
5:30 P.M.

Dr. Larry Saidman, the anesthesiologist who would be working my case the next morning, dropped by for his routine pre-op visit later that afternoon and became concerned immediately. He didn't like what he saw at all. Sweat was beading up on my forehead and running in rivulets down the sides of my face. My hands trembled, and I had trouble focusing on his words. Dr. Saidman checked my blood pressure; it had dropped to a perilously low 65/30.

The evidence was clear to him: My body was experiencing severe septic shock. My colon must have ruptured, leaking dangerous bacteria into my system. I was on the edge of delirium, and he recognized that my situation was now critical.

Dr. Saidman raced to the nurses' desk and called Dr. Peskin at home. "Gerald, we can't wait until morning. Rolf's become septic, and his condition is serious. We have to operate now!"

"I'm on my way," Dr. Peskin answered quickly. "Maybe thirty minutes at most."

Nurses and a host of doctors sprang into accelerated action, and by 6 p.m., I was lifted onto a gurney for the trip to the second-floor operating room. An orderly wheeled me to the elevator, followed by Helen and Colleen. I didn't know it, but my life hung in the balance.

As we waited for the elevator doors to open, a young intern joined the group. He gripped a piece of paper and a pen in his hand.

"I hate to bother you at a time like this, but my dad's a big fan of yours," he said, thrusting the pen and paper at me.

Helen couldn't believe his presumption. "For goodness sake, can't you see this isn't the time?"

Instinctively, I reached out for the paper and scribbled something that resembled my name just as the elevator doors opened.

Dr. Saidman began the anesthesia procedure at 6:15. Because of my weakened condition, he supplemented the usual assortment of anesthetic drugs with Intropin, a dopamine-like drug that raises blood pressure.

Dad and Mom, barred from the operating bay, found solace in Ingrid's room on the fifth floor.

Dr. Peskin arrived at 6:30, running from the parking lot. The five-man surgery team didn't waste any time and quickly cut a long incision down the middle of my stomach and opened me up for a look-see. After a short discussion, the decision was made to proceed with the resection. Approximately ten inches of my large intestine were snipped out as well as a few inches of my terminal ileum. The doctors then looked around for anything else that might appear to be troublesome. When they were satisfied they had done everything they could, the surgeons sewed the end of the ileum to the end of the transverse colon and began to close me up. It took three hours and forty minutes until the final stitch was done.

I had survived *and* dodged the ostomy bullet. Mom and Dad were there when I was rolled out of surgery and into the Intensive Care Unit at midnight. I, of course, was still in dreamland but smiled when I saw them. My parents were excited to see me and grateful to hear everything went well.

In the ICU, Mom and Dad stood on either side of the bed, each holding one of my hands. Although they knew I would not wake up for some time, they stayed by my side until 1:30 a.m. Finally, exhausted, they headed home. It had been a long and trying day for all of us.

As anticipated, I slept through the night, the anesthesia bringing a few hours of drugged peace. Little did I know, however, that my medical problems were just beginning.

The worst was yet to come.

Saturday, October 13
8:35 a.m.
In the Trauma Unit

When I struggled to open my eyes the next morning, I could hardly move. At first, I was aware of the intense pain in my abdomen, but then I realized I was hooked up to more tubes, bottles, drains, and IV bags than I could count. Strange clicking-like sounds distracted me, as the blood pressure monitor and respirator recorded my vital signs. I had an oxygen mask over my face and IV lines running from both arms and my neck. I felt like a marionette, connected to a bunch of strings.

The Trauma Unit was one big room, filled with a half-dozen patients, each separated by only a curtain—much like an emergency ward. There was twenty-four-hour supervision and monitoring machines everywhere. Because the patients received round-the-clock care in a well-lit room without windows, it was difficult to tell night from day.

The shift nurse noticed I was awake and came over from her monitoring station to check on me.

"Good morning, Rolf," she said with a strong European accent.

She must be German or Danish.

"How do you feel?" she asked, checking on my various monitors.

I wasn't sure. One thing was certain: I didn't feel like moving.

Nurse Carla van den Hour lifted the clear plastic oxygen mask from my face.

"Where am I?"

"You're in the Trauma Unit of the ICU," answered Carla. "It's a stop after surgery until you can go back to your regular floor."

"What's that groaning? It sounds like someone's dying," I asked.

She leaned over and whispered in my ear. "That's a very sick lady. There are four other very sick people in this ICU."

Carla took my vital signs. Temperature was high: 102 degrees. Pulse was also high: 130.

"What's this tube in my nose?" I was having a hard time talking with it.

"That's an NG tube, or nasogastric device. It extends through your nose, down your throat and into your stomach, draining the stomach's contents by suction. You see, the anesthesia you had usually stops the bowels from working after an operation like yours, at least for a while. The NG tube will prevent nausea and vomiting and will be removed in a few days," said the nurse.

She continued speaking. "You have several more tubes, brave young man. A couple of Penrose drains are connected to the side of your abdomen. They're collecting incisional drainage from around the resection area. A Foley catheter is catching your urine, and you'll have your ventilator until you can breathe easier on your own. You just might qualify for some kind of an award," she quipped.

I managed a faint smile. Nurse Van Hooten repositioned the oxygen mask. *Is this really happening to me? I've been healthy my entire life . . . and making my living as a professional athlete and only in my early twenties. How did I end up here—in this incredibly dehumanizing position?*

Before I could think further, I saw Nurse Van Hooten with her blood-drawing kit. *Not again.* I was aware of several needle stabs as she probed for an artery deep in my right wrist. It took her so long that her attempt left my wrist quivering and me clenching my teeth because the pain was way worse than a normal blood draw. My nurse needed arterial blood to check my blood gases. Unfortunately, she would need to repeat this unusually painful procedure daily on both wrists over the next week. (The procedure also left scars on my wrists that I carry to this day.)

"There you go," she said, as she finally finished and pocketed the vial. "I'll be over at the nurses' desk. We're here to assist you twenty-four hours a day. Don't hesitate to use the call button if we can help with anything."

Dad and Mom returned to the hospital at 9 a.m., still exhausted after only a few hours of sleep from the previous night. Word must've gotten out about my surgery as they had to answer numerous phone calls from friends and the media about my condition before they left the house.

In the meantime, Dad was also supposed to be preparing for a medical conference he would be presenting at in Copenhagen the following weekend. In many circles, Dad was much better known than me. In addition to heading the Pathology department at UC San Diego and directing the Center for Reproduction of Endangered Species at the San Diego Zoo, he was one of the world's leading authorities on the human placenta.

After spending a few minutes checking up on me, Dad slipped out of the ICU and headed toward his basement lab. He knew that the intestinal specimen removed from me would be waiting for him, and he was anxious to see what it would tell him. Dad was on a first-name basis with most of the lab techs.

"Hello, Kurt, nice to see you," said one of the older techs when he arrived. "We heard about Rolf. We're so sorry. How's he doing?"

"He made it through the night okay, and he's resting right now," Dad answered. "Are the tissue samples ready?"

"They sure are. You can view the slide of Rolf's colon under this microscope."

Before Dad examined the slides, however, he picked up what was left of my colon that was still lying on the cutting board and gently pulled it apart to scan the lining. The extent of the lesions on the inside lining of the intestinal wall horrified him. There was virtually no healthy section anywhere. *No wonder Rolf was in such pain*, he thought to himself. This was as bad as he had ever seen.

Next, Dad placed the slides under the microscope. He bent over and looked through the lens. He glanced up, thought for a minute, and then peered inside again.

"Anything unusual, Kurt?"

"Yes," he replied. "I don't believe Rolf has Crohn's disease. These tissue samples are consistent with ulcerative colitis. I believe he has been misdiagnosed."

My father groaned. Crohn's disease and resultant inflammation may occur anywhere along the digestive tract from the esophagus down to the small and large intestine, but ulcerative colitis affects *only* the large intestine. Both diseases are similar in the way they present symptomatically, but the biggest difference is that if you have ulcerative colitis and your entire colon is removed, you will never get the disease again. Not so with Crohn's disease.

WEDNESDAY, OCTOBER 17
9:15 A.M.

After major abdominal surgery, it's vital to expand the lungs and keep them clear to avoid pneumonia. That's why I was initially connected to a ventilator that forced me to take deep breaths.

With each heave, however, my lacerated stomach muscles burned terribly. There was no way I could lessen the discomfort, so I found myself anticipating each breath, knowing a shot of pain would follow immediately.

Dad returned at noon and waited with me for my much-anticipated morphine injection. The shot helped take the edge off the pain and allowed me to try to get out of bed and take a few steps—standard post-op procedure.

"First comes sitting up," he said, as he slowly raised the back of the hospital bed to a near vertical position.

"Oh!" I moaned.

"I know it hurts, but you have to do this."

Dad and a nurse lifted and slid my legs over the side of the bed. The floor looked like it was at the bottom of the Grand Canyon.

"Easy does it." Dad slowly eased my legs down and took hold of my arm. I caught my breath and steadied myself as I stood up, leaning on Dad.

"Now, take a few steps," Dad directed.

I grabbed an IV pole in one hand and Dad's arm in the other and shuffled my right foot, taking my first step. Then came a second . . . and a third . . . and a fourth step.

Those four steps felt like four laps around a 400-meter track.

"I don't think I can go any farther," I protested. "I'm getting dizzy."

"That's enough for now," Dad said. "Let's get you back into bed."

Later, under Dad's watchful eye, Dr. Peskin came by to examine my incision. He lifted the pus-filled dressing, and for the first time I saw the surgeon's work. My chest and belly had been shaved smooth, and now a neat line ran down the middle of my stomach. The incision was secured with nice tight sutures.

"It looks good," said Dr. Peskin proudly. "You're going to heal nicely, Rolf."

Mom stepped in the room. She had good news and bad news regarding my sister. Ingrid was fighting a fever and had to be catheterized. Despite her pain, however, she had written me a note: "I know what I've been going through hasn't been any fun, but it's certainly nothing compared to what you are dealing with. I'm thinking of you, and I hope I can come up and see you soon."

Just then, Dad was asked by a nurse to step outside for a phone call.

"Dr. Benirschke, this is Gene Klein," said the booming voice on the other end of the phone line. Although Dad didn't know much about pro football, he did know that Gene Klein was the owner of the San Diego Chargers.

"Yes, Mr. Klein, what can I do for you?"

"We just want you to know that we're all hoping and thinking good thoughts for Rolf over here. You've raised a fine young son, and we are all pulling for him. Please tell him there will always be a place for him with our club as long as I'm around."

"I'll be sure to pass that along, Mr. Klein. Thanks."

Early that evening, following another brief "walk" around my hospital room, my fever shot up to 103 and with it came fear that something might be wrong. Dad and Mom wondered about my feverish condition, but Dr. Peskin, on his evening rounds, didn't seem alarmed.

"I don't think you have anything to worry about," he said. "The fever spikings are natural and should begin to dissipate. Nothing has happened here to warrant any undue concern."

My parents had a lot to talk about that night. Their youngest son and only daughter were in the same hospital, two floors apart, both in a lot of pain following significant operations. They also knew that Mom's father, my grandfather who we called Opa, lay in another hospital in Germany, not expected to live more than a few months. On a non-medical note, Dad was scheduled to leave soon to deliver an important keynote speech in Copenhagen, one that had been planned for over a year.

"Even though my mother says not to come, I think I have to go," Mom said, clearly in a dilemma as to what to do. "It may be the last time I see my father alive, if the reports are correct."

"You're probably right, Marion. And I feel like I *have* to fulfill my obligation to speak in Copenhagen. But . . . ."

"Yes, what should we do?" she asked out loud.

Despite their other obligations, they were parents first and agreed that neither of them would leave me if things started to go sideways, which now seemed unlikely. Besides, my brother, Steve, who was still in medical school, had decided to fly in from Cleveland. He would be arriving in three days, and he would be here before my parents left and stay until they returned. His presence helped my parents make their decision. Unless I took a turn for the worse, Mom would fly to Munich and Dad would leave for Copenhagen as planned.

The night proved uneventful, and by early morning my temperature was back to normal. Oddly, when I woke up, I noticed my right eyelid was drooping profoundly. In addition, my neck and chest also seemed very swollen.

A blood work-up revealed an astonishingly high white blood cell count of 44,500, and concern immediately mounted that there was an infection somewhere in my system. A chest X-ray showed signs of a micro-lung collapse—the result of poor respiratory effort.

To take care of the latter problem, Drs. Peskin and Mowery ordered respiratory therapy to begin immediately and proceed every six hours. The therapy involved using a chest vibrator applied to my back to loosen mucus and fluids that might be building up in my lungs. I was instructed to cough as hard as I could to bring up any phlegm and keep expanding my lungs with the regular use of blow bottles.

Early that afternoon, Mom helped me on my first significant exercise in more than two days. We walked the length of the Trauma Unit and back. I didn't set any speed records, but the hundred-foot walk was an accomplishment—even for this professional athlete. I felt good about what I had done.

During my short walk, I peeked at the patient who had been making all of the noise next to me. I learned she was a Samoan princess who tipped the scales at 450 pounds. Her body, covered with tattoos, was filled with metastasized lymphatic cancer, and although she had undergone two successive major surgeries, the prognosis was not good. I felt badly for her, and it was sobering to think of all that she had been through.

Next to the tattooed princess was a young man who had been in a major motorcycle accident. His helmet had saved his life, but his arms and legs had all been broken, and they were now set in awkward-looking casts. Adjacent to him was another banged-up victim—a man who had plowed his car into a telephone pole.

"It kind of makes me feel like I have it pretty good," I said to Mom.

"Life isn't easy, Rolfie, and it certainly doesn't seem fair at times. Yes, we need to count our blessings."

Counting those blessings would become more difficult in the coming days.

7

Lightning Strikes

Intensive Care Unit patients are supposed to be off limits for visitors except for immediate family members. But that afternoon, an exception was made for a special guest—Coach Coryell.

The whispering of nurses by my bed woke me from a restless nap, and I was startled to see Coach Coryell standing there, talking to them. He had a pained expression on his face but smiled when he saw that I was awake. He was obviously nervous but tried to cover up his anxiousness with a warm but cautious greeting. He was definitely out of his element and likely had never seen one of his football players hooked up to a half-dozen whirring machines with tubes running everywhere.

"Hello, Rolf," he began awkwardly. "How are you feeling?"

I nodded, then whispered, "I guess I'm all right, considering the circumstances."

"I want you to know that all the guys and I want you to hurry up and get out of here. We're pulling for you. We want you back with us, where you belong."

"Thanks, Coach."

"I also have a little present here." Coach reached into a small equipment bag and pulled out a white No. 6 Chargers jersey. It was my game jersey.

As he held it up, I could see that my teammates had all scribbled their names on the jersey, some adding notes of encouragement:

Hang in there, Rolf
We're thinking of you
Get well soon!
We need you back

There was also a Bible verse—Proverbs 3:5—inscribed on the jersey: "Trust in the Lord with all your heart, and do not lean on your own understanding."

Each player's signature brought a special memory to mind, and I realized how much we had all been through together. I missed them.

Coach and I made small talk for a few minutes, and then it was time for him to go. It was clearly difficult for Coach Coryell to see one of his players so sick, but for me, his presence was very special and meant a lot—a visit I will never forget.

One of the nurses hung the jersey on the hospital wall in front of my bed so I could see it without moving my head. Seeing my game jersey every day reminded me of the kindness of my teammates and became a great source of inspiration, even though I believed I would never wear it again on a Sunday afternoon before a full stadium crowd.

After Coach Coryell left, Mom and Dad came by for their third visit of the day. When I pointed out my new prized wall hanging, they hardly noticed. I could tell something was troubling them.

"Should we really be going away next week?" Mom asked Dad in my presence.

Ah, so that was it. By the way she phrased her question, it was obvious she was having second thoughts about the wisdom of her and Dad both traveling to Europe at the same time.

"I've been wondering, too, Marion," said Dad. "We can't make a final decision yet. Let's wait a few more days and see how things are when Steve gets here."

Mom decided to change the subject.

"Some good news! Ingrid is feeling much better. She has gas pains from the anesthesia and still hurts some, but the doctors say she's turned the corner. She may even try to walk down to see you tomorrow."

"That would be nice." I forced a smile.

"And Steve is arriving Monday for sure," Dad said.

"That will be nice, too." *What would really be nice would be to finally get out of this ICU and back to my own room*, I thought. The Samoan woman never stopped moaning and groaning all night, and it was hard to get any sleep.

Mom still wasn't sure if she should leave and go visit her ailing father in Germany. "We really don't know what we should do," she confessed. "I don't feel good about this."

I could tell this was really tough on Mom and realized I could help put her at ease. "Mom, it sounds like Opa is in pretty bad shape. I think you should see him. He is getting older, and it might just be the last time you get to see him. Besides, Steve will be here and I'll be fine."

"Thank you for saying that," she replied.

My sleep was erratic that night—moments of peace interrupted by stretches of pain and chills. I'm sure I talked in my sleep, but it couldn't have been anything like the ghastly sounds still emanating from behind the neighboring curtain.

In the morning, Nurse Carla van den Hour noted that my face and neck appeared more bloated than usual, a sign that I may be retaining water. She checked my vital signs, but for the first time in weeks, my blood pressure and temperature were normal.

"Let's get you weighed." Carla pointed to the scale by the nurses' desk.

"Do we have to?" The scale was fifteen feet away.

"Yes, I'm afraid so."

With her help, I hobbled over to the scale and weighed in at 150 pounds—up nearly ten pounds in just twenty-four hours. Not a good sign. I was retaining water.

Carla notified a doctor, and I was immediately given Lasix, a diuretic that forces fluids to be expelled through increased urine output.

Upon returning to bed after my short walk, I began perspiring profusely and started to shake. Carla took my temperature; it had shot up to 102 in a matter of minutes. She quickly gave me cold, wet compresses for my forehead and aspirin to help control the fever.

Dad arrived at 9:30 a.m., just as Dr. Peskin was making his morning rounds with Dr. Lee Griffith, the Chief Resident. When they finished their examination of me, Dad followed them into the hallway.

Dad spoke first, expressing what had to be on all three doctors' minds. "He looks terrible, doesn't he?"

"The fluid infiltration is not good," Dr. Peskin said. "But the Lasix should help. I think we still have things under control. Rolf has been through a lot but seems to be doing as well as can be expected." When the doctors left, Dad bumped into Carla as she was coming out of the ICU.

"You look worried, Dr. Benirschke."

"Worried? Yes, I'm definitely concerned. This has been hard on all of us."

"I'm sure it has," she replied sympathetically.

"This has been especially hard on Marion. She can hardly sleep anymore. Last night was the worst. Thank goodness Ingrid is doing better, but poor Rolf . . . ."

Dad returned to my bedside. Seated in a chair, he tried to concentrate on some reading while I drifted in and out of consciousness, finding little peace in either state. It was difficult for Dad to just sit there and not be able to do more than read my charts and consult with the doctors. For one of the first times in Dad's life, all his knowledge and all his connections couldn't help the one patient he cared most about—his son. He was powerless to do anything, and that had to be torturing him.

While tossing and turning, I suddenly blurted out, "Dad, I've got to get dressed!"

"Dressed for what?" my father asked.

"The game! I've got to get into the game. Coach just called for the field goal unit!"

"That's not possible. Rolf, you're having a dream."

"But Coach needs me in there. He's depending on me!"

"Rolf, wake up. You're in a hospital bed."

"What?!" I looked around at my surroundings, slowly awakening from my dream. "Who put me here?" I asked, still a bit confused.

"You're in the hospital. The Chargers are playing Seattle today, but you're not going to be there."

"Oh."

My head slumped back onto my pillow. I was really disoriented. The morphine was playing serious tricks with my mind.

Later that morning, I was taken for a chest X-ray. My lungs did not look good, which meant the diuretic was acting slower than the doctors had hoped for.

After an afternoon walk around the nurses' station, I looked into a mirror and was shocked at my dark eyes, sad and lifeless and empty. My life had changed forever that evening when Dr. Peskin had been forced to perform the emergency surgery that saved my life. I had lost more than half of my colon; I had lost the innocence of youth. Instead of worrying about football games and Friday night dates and hanging out at the beach, I was worrying about blood draws, IV lines, and a hideous scar down my abdomen. I was also still pondering some terrifying questions:

Will I survive?

If I do, what kind of life will I have?

Will I ever be able to play sports again?

Will I ever enjoy a run on the beach or a swim in the ocean?

The questions were overwhelming, so I tried not to dwell on them and fought hard to think about something else. I was brought back to the present when intern resident Cammy Mowery came in to check my vital signs.

"This is a total bummer," I complained to Dr. Mowery. "I mean, look at me."

Cammy smiled. "You don't look so bad. You just think you do. The drugs are causing the bloating, and we can wash your hair today. That should help."

Since the Trauma Unit had no television sets, Dad had brought in a portable TV that afternoon so we could watch the Chargers play Seattle. Mom joined us for the kickoff.

At halftime, Dad tried to help me out of bed for another short walk. But the pain of sliding off the bed and standing up was so excruciating that I needed to sit down and rest before getting started. Dad picked up his camera again.

"Smile!"

Click.

"Dad! Do you have to?"

Click.

Decades later, those pictures still serve as a gruesome remembrance of that difficult time and help remind me just how lucky I am today.

"You look better, Rolfie," Dad said. "Remarkably better than five hours ago." The diuretic was starting to do its job.

SISTER ACT

At five o'clock that afternoon, Ingrid and I saw each other for the first time since she had arrived at University Hospital five days earlier. An orderly had wheeled her into the Trauma Unit to say hello, and she was clearly shocked by what she saw.

"Oh, Rolf! I—"

"Ingrid!"

She held my arm against her cheek. "I was going to tell you some good news," Ingrid said. "I'm having my IV removed tomorrow, so I may be getting out of here in a day or two. But after seeing you, what I'm going through seems like nothing."

She searched for a safe subject to talk about.

"Are they treating you okay?" she asked.

"Sometimes yes, sometimes no. It's mostly this place." I jerked my head toward the curtained walls and the noise coming from the other patients.

We talked for a short time before the orderly returned to take her back upstairs to her room. "If there is anything I can do, I should be out soon. I'd be happy to do anything to help," Ingrid said.

"Just your coming to visit was great," I replied, already feeling tired and ready to doze off.

Mom and Dad stopped back a short time later for one last little walk before they headed home. Dad helped me out of bed and into a chair again. Then he supported me as I shuffled around the hospital halls, tubes, and bottles hanging from my IV pole. The journey lasted ten minutes, but I couldn't wait to get back in bed. I was exhausted.

Rolf looks weak, but he seems to be improving, Dad thought, trying to convince himself that I was on the mend.

Dr. Peskin was thinking the same thing when he consulted with Dad in the hallway. "I think the best thing we can do is to let him sleep as much as he can and let nature take its course," he shared. "We still need more time."

"What do the latest blood and urine labs show?" Dad asked curiously.

"Well, actually they don't look great," Dr. Peskin admitted. "The blood culture shows *E. coli,* and several other bacteria are present in abundance in his bloodstream, but we can't figure out the source of the infection."

MONDAY, OCTOBER 22
10 A.M.

After a fitful night that was interrupted way too often by nurses checking my IV fluids and the monitors that seemed to start beeping just as I fell back asleep, I woke up mid-morning with Dr. Peskin standing next to my bed. He needed to check my sutures and irrigate and clean my twelve-inch incision with Betadine.

After carefully pulling off the bandages, I saw the wound again. This time the incision looked awful. I actually had to look away as the ugly cut still appeared open, up to half an inch in some areas. But Dr. Peskin didn't seem to think anything was out of the ordinary and pronounced everything fine. He explained that my incision would slowly granulate in, meaning it would heal from the inside out and gradually close.

After the surgeon left, I found myself alone behind the curtain wall with Nurse Carla van den Hour as she gently bandaged me back up. She had become a favorite of mine, earning my trust for the way she had handled some very difficult and painful situations. Now I really needed someone to talk to.

"Is there hope?" I asked in a hushed voice. "Am I going to make it?"

"What do you mean, is there hope?" Carla feigned annoyance.

"They're talking about taking out the stitches, but the wound isn't close to being healed. Am I going to get out of here soon?"

"Maybe."

"But Carla, if that's true, then why do I still hurt so much? I still need regular shots of morphine to take the edge off the pain before I take my walks and even during the nights to help me sleep. This sucks!"

"Time," she said quietly. "It takes time to heal. You've only been here a little while and have been through a lot. Keep fighting. You're going to get there."

The next morning, Dad and Mom came in just as I was completing my morning walk.

"You look troubled," Dad noticed.

"I'm exhausted," I panted. "We just walked fifteen yards, and if I can't do that without getting tired . . . ."

Mom interrupted my thoughts.

"Rolf, you're shaking."

She was right. My body had suddenly started to shake uncontrollably, and my body had began and sundenly started chattering violently. My parents quickly helped me slide back into bed and covered me up with blankets. I was frightened and in excruciating pain again. It felt like my incision was about to be ripped open from top to bottom.

Dad quickly called for the nurse while I begged Mom for more blankets. I was freezing. But when the nurse arrived, she recognized my symptoms and took a quick check of my temperature. It had risen to 103 degrees, confirming that I was spiking a fever.

Little did I know that I would repeat these horrible shakes, chills, and fever spikes countless times over the next ten days. Although I would get very cold, my temperature would soar to 103 or 104 degrees—dangerously high. The nurses would work hard to bring my temperature down as quickly as they could, but each episode lasted thirty minutes or more and left me physically exhausted—and terribly frightened.

What was happening to me?

I was given more morphine, and as my shaking subsided, I drifted off into a fitful sleep. By afternoon, my white blood count had dropped to an encouraging 10,900, barely above the normal 10,000 and way down from 44,500 two days earlier. Whatever internal infection I had been fighting seemed to now be under control.

Then Ingrid dropped by, excited because her IV had been removed and because she was eating solid food again. She was on the mend.

"But the really good news is that I get to go home tomorrow," she said.

"Great! I wish I was going with you." I really meant it.

Suddenly, my breathing became very labored, and I could sense Ingrid's concern.

"Rolf, are you okay?"

"I'm not sure. It's like I'm not getting enough air—"

Ingrid quickly moved her wheelchair toward the nurses' desk, where Sheana Funkhauser had just come on duty.

"Nurse! Nurse! Rolf's having a hard time breathing!"

Sheana ran to my bed and immediately reinstalled the nasal prongs I had taken out of my nostrils. The direct flow of oxygen slowly restored my breathing to normal.

"Easy to fix, fortunately," Sheana said. She looked at my chart and noticed that over the weekend my oxygen mask had been removed. "I wonder why they did that," she said out loud. "The surgery wasn't that long ago."

"Maybe they thought he was getting better," Ingrid offered.

"Rolf *is* getting better, but it's always a good idea to be a little conservative in these kinds of things."

When the nurse left, I confided several dark thoughts to Ingrid.

"Oh, Ingrid, I hate the ICU. I can never tell if it's day or nighttime. The lights are always on, and I have a really hard time sleeping because people are always checking up on me. I hate the noises, the smells, and being in the same room with all these sick people. It's awful!"

As if on cue, the Samoan woman let out a low moan, followed by a gasping shriek.

"Just like that!" I said. "I know she's in pain, but it's hard to have to hear it all the time."

That night, Mom called the nursing station and the nurse brought me the phone. She said that my brother, Steve, had just landed at the airport and would drop by in the morning. She also told me that she had called Germany and learned that her father was really not doing well.

"Opa could die soon," said Mom. She paused as she considered her next words. "This is hard, but we won't decide until tomorrow night whether I'm going to Germany and if Dad will fly to Copenhagen. If you or Ingrid don't want us to go, we won't make either trip, even if that means not being able to say goodbye to Opa."

"I want you to see Opa," I pleaded. "And I want Dad to give his talk in Copenhagen . . . they're counting on him. I mean that. I'm getting better, and besides, Steve will be here."

When our conversation ended, I carefully placed the phone on the cradle and stared at the ceiling.

I was messing up a lot of people's lives, and I didn't feel good about any of it.

8

HE AIN'T HEAVY

TUESDAY, OCTOBER 23
9 A.M.

Five days after my surgery, my brother, Steve, arrived at the hospital and was escorted to the ICU to see me. Even though we had been competitive brothers as youngsters, we had matured and put all that behind us.

"Thanks for coming, buddy." I put my left hand over Steve's. "I appreciate your taking time off from med school and coming all the way out from Cleveland."

"I *had* to come," Steve said. "There's no way I could have stayed away, especially with Mom and Dad leaving for Europe."

"You arrived just in time," I continued, shaking my head. "There are some good people here, especially some of the nurses, but it hasn't been a picnic. I'm worn out from all of the blood draws, bandage changes, and no sleep, and the pain just doesn't seem to be letting up."

I told him the worst was when they needed arterial blood to check my carbon dioxide and oxygen levels. Normally when you give blood, a nurse finds a vein in the crook of your arm, gives it a quick stab, and then fills a syringe with blood. But arterial blood must be drawn from an artery, and the best place to find one is in your wrist, underneath a protective layer of tendons and muscle.

"This one nurse jabbed the needle into my wrist and then moved it around until she found the artery," I said to my brother. "I can't tell you how painful it was until she got it right."

After relating that story, I also told Steve about the many times my doctors and residents examined my surgical incision, which necessitated them removing and reapplying my bandages each time. It was getting to be a bit much, and I was worn out . . . and it hurt each time.

"You have to remember that University Hospital is a teaching hospital," my brother explained. "Residents and interns without a lot of experience will be coming by to see you at all hours. It's how they learn."

"Yeah, I know. But I'm getting a little tired of being the guinea pig. Why can't they coordinate their visits so I don't have to have my dressings taken off and put back on several times each day when somebody new comes in and wants to take a look? Don't they know it hurts?"

"Tell you what," Steve said. "Let me see what I can do."

My brother left my room to use the telephone near the elevator to call Dr. Peskin.

When he finally got through, Dr. Peskin asked Steve how I was doing. "He doesn't look great, is still in a fair amount of pain, but worse is how depressed he seems," Steve responded. "That worries me more than the way he looks. And he's complaining about how the residents and interns are stopping in all the time. Is there something you can do about that?"

Dr. Peskin said he'd try to minimize the intrusions. As for my depression, he said he would keep an eye on my mental outlook but would take a wait-and-see approach.

In mid-afternoon, I had to go to the bathroom but needed assistance getting out of bed. Nurse Sheana came, and with her supporting my skinny frame, I slowly hobbled over to the nearby bathroom.

Just past the nurses' station, I lost control and had an accident. A smelly brown mess slowly leaked down my leg and onto the floor.

"I'm so sorry!" I was angry and embarrassed at what had just happened. "I hate this!"

"Don't get upset," Sheana said. "You *are* sick, and when you're sick, these things happen. It's nothing to get upset about."

"But it's so humiliating."

When Sheana helped me back into bed, I noticed that the front of her uniform was soiled. Enough was enough! I turned my face to the wall, tears streaming down my cheek, while I heard her and two other nurses mop up the floor. *Dear God, when will this all end?*

At 9 p.m., Dad visited the Trauma Unit. Mom stayed home to finish packing since they would both be leaving in the morning on separate flights to Europe. "How are you, son?" he asked.

"I had kind of a shaky afternoon, but I'm okay. I'm really glad that Steve is here though."

"Well, you actually look pretty good," said Dad, noticing that the puffiness around my face and neck had dissipated. The diuretics had done their job, and I was back to my "frail and gaunt" self again.

"Since your condition has stabilized, Mom feels better about going to Munich tomorrow, while I fly to Copenhagen. I hope you understand why we have to go."

"Dad, I'll be fine. Really."

Life had to go on.

WEDNESDAY, OCTOBER 24
10:30 A.M.

The first key to the mystery of my unexplained fevers was revealed on this morning. The results of the blood cultures, taken from the previous day, indicated the presence again of gram-negative organisms. Somehow, *E. coli* bacteria were getting into my bloodstream. The news raised two questions:

• Where were the organisms originating?

• What antibiotics would be effective?

Early that afternoon, I started having a series of watery, green-colored bowel movements, all of which were followed by severe cramping.

I slept reasonably well that night, but when I got up in the morning, I had another embarrassing accident on the way to the toilet. Carla van den Hour took my temperature, and it had risen three degrees (to 102 degrees) after my bathroom trek.

"What's the use? Tell me, what's the use?" I was feeling sorry for myself again.

"This is a tough time, Rolf."

"I'm tired of being a bother and messing on floors. I must be such a pain."

"You're not a pain," Carla reassured me. "We'll get through this. Look, it may seem like you've been in this place forever, but how long has it been since you were admitted? Two weeks? And how long since your surgery? One week?"

I didn't answer her. The pain in my gut felt as though someone was jabbing me with a sharp knife again.

A bit later, Steve arrived and read my chart while standing at the foot of my bed. He stopped when he saw the notation about the *E. coli* in my blood.

"Have you had any more fevers?" he asked.

"Yes. Why?"

"Well, you have bacteria in your system that you shouldn't have."

"What does that mean?"

"It means that you either have an abscess, or there is a leak in the anastomosis line. Whatever it is, we need to find out right away. This is the complication that causes people to die from this operation. If we can't get a handle on the bacteria, they can multiply so rapidly that they can overcome your body's defense system very quickly."

Steve added that it was critical to identity the organisms and find the appropriate antibiotics. He explained that the bacteria can quickly become resistant, and, as a result, the antibiotics must be changed continually. "This is where we really have to rely on the hospital's infectious disease department," Steve explained.

"Are they good?"

"Dad said they're the best around. I also see here that Peskin has scheduled you for another ultrasound. I'm going to talk to him to see if he's considered doing a dye study on you. That's where they inject methylene blue into your system, and together with the ultrasound, they'll be able to find out if you have a leak in your bowel or if there is a pocket of infection somewhere."

I could tell Steve was very concerned, and his changed demeanor was unsettling.

A short time later, it was time for my ultrasound. Steve helped escort me to the diagnostic room. Clearly worried, he kept a brotherly hand on my shoulder as the orderly gently pushed my gurney down the halls.

"This won't hurt. I promise," he comforted me.

Three hours later, I was back in my bed in the ICU. The tests hadn't hurt much, but my stomach still felt awful. A doctor from the infectious disease department arrived shortly afterward and gave me a new series of antibiotics through my IV.

I was encouraged that they seemed to be on top of the situation, but what lifted my spirits more was seeing a sackful of mail in the corner. Although I was too weak to open any of the letters, just the thought of so many people taking the time to write an encouraging card almost choked me up.

THURSDAY, OCTOBER 25
8:30 A.M.

Drs. Peskin, Griffith, and Mowery arrived together on morning rounds.

"The nurses tell me you won't take the Maalox, which could help your gas pains." Dr. Peskin spoke with a slight smile.

"I tried, but that stuff makes me gag. Ever since I was young, I've had a hard time taking pills or medication. Now that I'm sick, it's almost impossible."

"I understand, but the Maalox could really help," Dr. Peskin responded.

"Doesn't matter. I just can't get it down."

Knowing he was licked, Dr. Peskin changed the subject.

"Rolf, the good news is that the ultrasound scan of your abdomen doesn't show anything, but the bad news is that we know something's not quite right. Normally, at this stage after an operation, a patient is feeling much better and things are beginning to return to normal."

That was not what was happening to me. Besides the very loose stools, I was spiking high fevers, and tests were continuing to detect an increasing number of bacteria in my blood. Something was definitely not right.

"What's going on?" I asked.

"Well, we're not sure. Unfortunately, we're going to have to go back in and find out," Dr. Peskin said matter-of-factly.

"You mean another surgery? Laying me open *again*?" I couldn't believe what I was hearing.

"Yes. There's something clearly wrong, and we have to find out what it is and fix it. I can only tell you that a week after surgery, you should be getting better, not worse."

As my surgeon left the room, a slew of thoughts raced through my mind. I couldn't understand why I wasn't improving. Now I was facing another operation: general anesthesia, the scalpel, the dreaded NG tube—and more morphine. It was back to square one again. I wondered if I could get myself up for a second operation.

Really wondered . . . I was on empty . . . but I didn't have a choice.

Later that afternoon, I had dozed off when youth pastor Jim Adkins, my good friend, dropped by again. Sheana Funkhauser pulled him aside before she let him visit me.

"Jim, he's as down as I've seen him since he's been here," the nurse confided. "He keeps talking about dying. He's scared and really discouraged."

"Did something happen?" Jim thought he was coming to visit me as I was on the mend. "What's caused him to start feeling this way?" the concerned minister asked.

"The doctors told him they need to operate again because he's really not getting better. But even without that news, it's not hard to figure out why he's feeling so miserable. His white blood count has shot way up again, meaning there's still a major infection going on that his body is trying to fight. We just don't know where the infection is coming from. That is why they need to operate again."

Jim shook his head. He had seen my faith grow over the past year, but he must have wondered if I was strong enough to survive this latest devastating setback.

"Rolf seems to be losing his will to fight, which is almost understandable given all that he has gone through," Sheana explained. "He's telling me that he doesn't care anymore. He feels like he has no dignity left, and he doesn't want to be a burden to the nursing staff. He also said he had always felt in control, until now. He believes that if this is the time he is meant to go, then he's ready."

They moved closer to my bed. Sheana leaned over and whispered, "Rolf . . . you have a visitor."

My eyes slowly flickered open. "Hey, Jim, how are you?" I mumbled, trying to collect myself.

"The question is, how are *you*, Rolf? Sheana tells me you've been struggling a bit."

"She's not lying. There's not really much to feel good about these days." My voice cracked as I avoided eye contact with Jim.

"I hear you've really been through it and just got some tough news. I'm sorry. I want you to know that a lot of people really care about you and are praying for your recovery."

The tears were now flowing freely down my cheeks. I turned my head away. "Jim, I don't deserve those prayers. I feel like God's left me alone to struggle through this disease by myself. I don't feel like I can fight anymore. On top of that, I'm making it really hard for a lot of nice people, and I hate that."

"What do you mean?" Jim asked gently.

"Remember Helen, the nurse from upstairs? Well, she checked in on me during her break, and all I did was complain to her. I mean, she's one of the nicest, most caring people here, and I was such a jerk."

"I guarantee you Helen understands," Jim said, trying to console me. "She's seen hundreds of people go through some of the toughest things life has to offer. She knows exactly what you're dealing with, as does Jesus. He knows exactly where you are. Could we pray together?"

That sounded like a great idea. "Jim, would you pray that I don't lose my will to fight? I need help right now."

I felt broken, and ahead of me was a dark abyss of unknown. I really didn't want to die.

The Samoan princess was moaning loudly when Jim bowed his head and led the three of us in prayer. He had to pause several times to be heard, but it didn't matter. When Jim said "Amen," we gave each other a squeeze of the hand, and I thanked him for coming.

LIFTING DEAD WEIGHT

Ingrid arrived about a half hour after Jim Adkins left.

"Good news," she bubbled. "I'm outta here. I got my walking papers a few minutes ago."

"That's not good news, that's *great* news," I said, forcing a smile.

We tried to chitchat for a short time, but I dozed off to sleep in the middle of our conversation. I woke up a short time later with an urge to go to the bathroom. Sheana and another nurse helped me cross the room, but I became dizzy and wobbly and started to fall just as I lost control of my bowels . . . again. Before I slumped to the floor, the nurses caught my dead-weight, 135-pound body and gently helped me back to bed. They tried to comfort my fears and frustration as they cleaned me up, but I was humiliated and frightened, and I quickly became despondent.

My doctors were alerted to the latest episode, as was Steve. Just before midnight, San Diego time, Steve received a phone call from Dad in Copenhagen, where it was mid-morning.

"How is he?" my father asked.

"Dad, I'm afraid Rolf has taken a turn for the worse. It looks like he has real bad sepsis. It appears his bowel is leaking somewhere into his abdomen."

"Are they going to operate?" Dad understood the seriousness of the situation.

"Yes, and it may happen as soon as tomorrow. His fever's been going up and down like a yo-yo, especially after he gets out of bed and tries to take a walk of any kind. Right now, it's back up to 102 degrees, and he has those awful shaking chills again. The doctors are concerned and think he might have an abscess or a leak."

"My God, Steve! Now I wish we hadn't gone! Mom will be very upset when she hears this."

After hanging up, Dad sat in shock, wondering what was happening to his family. He decided he needed to call Mom in Tutzing, a small town outside of Munich, to tell her the latest about my situation. Upon hearing the news, she immediately wanted to return to San Diego on the next plane.

"But how is your father?" Dad asked, reminding her why she had decided to travel.

"He's not good. Not good at all. He's not expected to pull through this. But what are they saying about Rolf?" she asked, quickly changing the subject.

"He's stable at the moment, but they're not sure what is going on. Marion, I know you want to go home, but there's nothing you can do in San Diego. Why don't you stay where you are and be with your dad for a few days? I'm able to cut my trip short and head back tomorrow morning, right after my talk. That should put me back home by tomorrow night."

They agreed that was what they should do.

FRIDAY, OCTOBER 26
EARLY MORNING HOURS

The beginning of my fourth week in University Hospital was a miserable one. The pain was constant, and so were the cramps. The longest period of rest seemed like just minutes.

"I can't take this much more," I told the night nurse. I was complaining again.

"The morning is almost here," she said with an understanding manner. "Things will seem better in the morning."

When Drs. Peskin and Griffith came by a short time later, they examined my chart and the results from the latest labs. They quickly determined that surgery could not wait.

"We have to go in right away," Dr. Peskin said. "Alert Dr. Saidman, and then have the operating room staff clear the way. And call Steve Benirschke and tell him what's happening."

Within thirty minutes, Steve had rushed into the Trauma Unit, unshaven and not wearing socks. It was 10 a.m.

"What's the story?" he asked Nurse Carla van den Hour.

"We put Rolf on some new antibiotics this morning, which seemed to have stabilized him. But he's not very coherent. He's talking a lot of gibberish. He thought I was Sheana when I first walked in."

Steve bent over my bed, his head just inches away from my face.

He had to see for himself.

"How ya doing, Rolf?" he asked.

"No! No!" I moaned, violently shaking my head. "Oh, God!"

Steve tried to explain to me that they were going to have to do another operation, but my scrambled mind couldn't comprehend the words he spoke.

"Rolf, listen to me. The internal suture line where they sewed your intestines together, the anastomosis, must have broken down. It is likely leaking bacteria into your abdominal cavity. They don't have an option. They need to find out what's wrong and correct it right away."

I started to come out of my fog. "I can't go through all this again."

"It's not an option, Rolf. It just isn't." Steve was firm, but understanding. "You've got to get up for this one more time. A lot of this depends on your will to fight."

Dr. Peskin walked in and said hello, trying his best to sound cheerful. Then he lifted the surgical dressings and examined the eight-day-old surgical opening.

"I know it's hard to believe right now, but you're going to feel a lot better when it's all done." Steve was trying to encourage me.

"I've heard that before!"

"You will feel better. Believe me, you will."

I dozed off after they left, exhausted. Ingrid arrived after getting a call from Steve. Together they huddled and discussed what they should be doing. They decided they needed to call Copenhagen and update Dad. Steve finally got through to the desk clerk at Dad's hotel, but there was a language barrier. The clerk only spoke German, so Steve quickly handed the phone to Ingrid, who was fluent in the language, to see if the clerk could connect them with Dad.

Dad had left word that he was off speaking at the medical conference. "It's urgent," Ingrid told the desk clerk. "Please leave a message that his son Rolf is going into surgery soon. Ask him to call Steve or Ingrid at University Hospital as soon as he can. Danke schön."

I was rolled into the surgery bay at around 2 p.m., accompanied by Dr. Saidman, the anesthesiologist, and a host of doctors. "What, no autographs this time?" he quipped. "You must be losing your popularity."

I looked up at him. "Beat the Broncos," I said.

The kid is losing it, thought the doctor.

But then my autograph *was* wanted. Dr. Mowery handed me a pen and paper and told me to sign it.

"What for?" I asked.

"It's a medical consent form. Routine," she said.

"Okay." I feebly scribbled my name.

At the bottom of the consent form was a typewritten annotation stating the possibility that the surgery team may have to perform an ileostomy, if the physicians deemed it necessary.

I was too drugged-out to read it, but if I had been lucid, I would have asked about the odds for such an outcome. I would have wanted to be mentally prepared for such a life-changing operation, just as I would for a game-winning kick. In my fleeting subconscious, however, I thought I was just going to have my gut re-opened to find out what was wrong with me.

The surgery bay—like a walk-in refrigerator—was cold. A nurse quickly covered my shivering body with two heated blankets to make me as comfortable as possible. I looked around at all the steel reflecting the bright lights in the operating room. *Wasn't I just here? This is like a déjà vu experience. I wonder if I'm going to wake up from this.*

"We're going to start the anesthesia now," announced Dr. Saidman, interrupting my morbid thoughts. "Name ten players on your team."

"Dan Fouts . . . Charlie Joiner . . . Kellen Winslow . . . Louie Kelcher . . . Hank Bauer . . . ."

I was under.

9

No Turning Back

The surgical team, headed by Dr. Peskin, didn't waste any time. Going through the same incision they had made eight days earlier, they opened me back up and examined the inside of my abdominal cavity.

They quickly found the problem. A small leak at the suture line where the ileum and the colon had been reconnected had enlarged into a bigger hole. The contents of my bowel and the bacteria that normally lived inside my gut were now spilling into my abdomen and getting into my bloodstream, creating a life-threatening situation.

No wonder I had been in so much pain and was spiking such high fevers, especially after my feeble attempts to walk. I was told later that it was a miracle I had survived to this point and that any delay in doing the second surgery would have been fatal.

Steve was a surgical observer for the first half hour, but finally the tension became unbearable. He retreated to the waiting room to be with Ingrid and explained to her what I had been experiencing.

At 5 p.m., Dad called from Copenhagen, where it was two o'clock in the morning. My brother took the call.

After catching up for a moment, my father asked, "Can you give me an update on Rolf?" He was hoping for some sign of optimism.

"They appear to have found the problem, Dad. It's a good thing they went in when they did."

"What did the doctors find?"

"It seems the anastomosis has broken down," Steve responded. "From what Peskin says, when they removed the diseased colon and reconnected the two ends together eight days ago, a leak must have developed along the suture line. Apparently, the combination of the disease and the long period of time Rolf has been on prednisone must have made his tissue a little like a sponge. The sutures just didn't hold. That little leak has opened more, so he is now septic and full of peritonitis. The last week must have been hell on him, battling that infection as best his weakened body could. I don't know how he's made it."

"Oh, my." Dad was stunned by the news and understood why his son was in critical condition. My life was in the balance, and all the worries about whether I would wake up with an ostomy seemed insignificant.

Steve recognized the same thing. "If Rolf survives, he's going to be wearing a bag, but that isn't the concern right now."

Dad agreed. "We can deal with that if it happens," he said. "Right now, he just has to get through this operation. The next forty-eight hours are critical. The medical team has to stay on top of the infection and figure out what antibiotics will work . . . if he survives the operation. You can't believe how far away and helpless I feel right now, being here in Copenhagen," he sighed.

"Dad, I feel just as helpless, and I can see the operating room from where I'm standing. I'll get back in touch as soon as we have any news."

Down the hall, Dr. Peskin was continuing to probe my abdominal cavity.

"Look at the infection!" Dr. Peskin exclaimed. "We're just in time. If we had waited any longer, the Chargers would be looking for a new kicker."

"Nurse, more suction," Dr. Griffith said. "We were hoping this wouldn't happen, but it's clear now Rolf needs an ostomy."

The doctors carefully snipped another couple of inches off the end of my ileum, then began plotting their next move: cutting an opening for the stoma into my right side. Normally, ostomy surgeries are well planned, and careful attention is paid to where the stoma hole is placed on the body. Stomas are generally situated below the belt line, where patients are least impacted when they bend and move. The appliances collecting fecal waste are not restricted and are more out of the way.

Because of the emergency nature of my situation, placement of my stomas was not a high priority . . . my doctors needed to get the life-saving procedure done as quickly as possible. As a result, I would end up with a poorly placed stoma that would make my post-op life much more difficult.

The doctors had a second problem—what to do with the remaining but non-functioning part of my colon. I was told later that the surgical team felt my situation was too critical to have the rest of my colon removed . . . that the operation would've taken too long. My doctors were forced to take what was left of my colon and create a second stoma on my left side. Although this stoma looked the same as my ileostomy, nothing would be going through it, and this stoma would remain a non-functioning mucous fistula colostomy. I would, nonetheless, be obligated to wear a small bag to collect the draining mucous that would be created by the normal sloughing off of the lining of the remaining colon.

It took the doctors more than four hours to complete the complex and tricky operation. When my midsection was finally ready to be closed up, they were forced to employ a novel way of suturing the stomach. In addition to the traditional string stitches, the doctors sewed me together with thirteen "piano wire" sutures. The heavy-gauge wire was inserted on one side of the wound, brought underneath the incision to the other side of the wound, and then twisted together. The tie-offs extended nearly two inches above my stomach.

The wire sutures could not completely close the incision, however, as the wound needed to heal by granulating in from the inside out. A nearly one-inch gap still existed the length of the incision. The doctors and nurses would pack the gaping incision with dressings dipped in Betadine, an antibacterial solution to keep them from becoming infected. These dressings would have to be changed twice a day, and the painful process would take my breath away each time the wound was repacked.

Ileostomy Surgery Today

A question I get asked often when I speak is, "Rolf, how has ileostomy surgery changed since you underwent the procedure thirty-five years ago?

Answer: While the operation is pretty much the same, most hospitals now have WOC (wound, ostomy, and continence) nurses who specialize in taking care of ostomy patients. They are almost always consulted by the doctor before the operation to help mark on the patient's abdomen where the stoma will be placed, and the nurses are there to assist patients in learning about how to use their appliance as they recover.

There have also been advancements in surgical techniques. Today, there are about 120,000 ostomy surgeries performed every year in the U.S., but only about 80,000 are permanent. For certain types of illness or injury, a J-pouch becomes an option that requires only a temporary ileostomy for three to six months before the patient is reconnected to an internally constructed J-pouch.

The other big differences now are the types of ostomy products being made. They are very individualized, quick and easy to change, rarely leak, never smell, and can be very low profile. Patients are generally able to return to whatever activity they enjoyed before their operation, and most people would never know a person is wearing an appliance unless they were told.

POST-OP

At 8:30 p.m., Steve and Ingrid called Dad back at his Copenhagen hotel, where it was nearing dawn. Dad, who had barely slept all night, grabbed the phone on the first ring, but the connection was lousy.

"Dad, it's us with good news!" Ingrid exclaimed.

"What happened?" Dad was fully alert now.

Steve took the phone. "Rolf just came out of surgery. He's not out of the woods yet, but Peskin says everything went well in the operating room. He needed quite a few blood transfusions, but he's doing okay."

"That's great news. Did they have to do an ileostomy?"

"Yes. It ended up being what we thought. He's going to be one sore guy when he comes around, which should be in an hour or so, but at least he made it through the operation. He's been in post-op now for ten minutes."

"Okay," my relieved father said. "I'm leaving for the airport this morning, and if all goes well, I'll be back in San Diego tomorrow night your time. I'll call Mom with the update. Now that Rolf has survived the operation and I'm coming home early, I'll tell her to stay in Tutzing until she's ready to leave."

In the recovery room, I slept quietly on my back, the anesthesia still doing its job. A total of nine devices were attached to my body. Besides the usual IV lines and Foley catheter to my bladder, two rubber catheters called "Red Robinsons" had been inserted next to my incision to irrigate the abdominal cavity. Near the bottom of the incision, two larger rubber catheters, called Chaffin-Pratt drains, were removing excess fluids.

I was moved to the Trauma Unit just after 11 p.m., about the same time television and radio stations around San Diego were leading their broadcasts with news about my emergency surgery. I was listed in "critical condition," the news anchors reported, but neither the hospital nor the family were releasing further details.

Nurse Sheana Funkhauser greeted me as my gurney was rolled back into the Trauma Unit.

"It's great to see you. We prayed that you would be brought back to us safely," she said with a wide smile.

I managed to say her name—"Sheana"—before several pairs of hands carefully slid me off the cart and onto my bed. I soon fell asleep, unaware that my life would never be the same.

SATURDAY, OCTOBER 27
7:30 A.M.

Drs. Peskin, Griffith, and Mowery were back early, as was Steve. They examined the long ugly wound that started just under my sternum and traveled past my belly button to just above my pubic bone. The large wire sutures added a surreal Frankenstein look.

At this point, I was still heavily sedated and far too drowsy to know or care what was going on, but I did get a glance at my incision.

"Can you hear me, Rolf?" Dr. Peskin asked.

I muttered something, but it was apparent I was a million miles away.

Steve reached over and gently clutched my hand. "Hang in there, buddy," he said.

Not until the early afternoon did I finally wake up from my drug-induced sleep. When my eyes focused, I saw Ingrid leaning over my bed, smiling at me.

"Hi there, good looking," she chirped. "Glad you made it! Dad is on his way home and should be here this evening."

"Great," I said, my lips cracking. "It seems like a long time since I've seen him or Mom."

"Well, Mom is going to stay a little while longer with Opa. I know it seems a lot longer to you, but they only left on Wednesday."

"And today is . . . ."

"Saturday. That's four days ago."

Steve joined Ingrid at the side of my bed.

"You're looking a heckuva lot better now than you did this morning," my older brother said, shaking his head.

"But I feel awful, like I'm burning up inside. It hurts more than it did yesterday or the day before. And I saw the wire sutures. Wow. I can't believe they sewed me up with wire! How are they going to get those things out?"

Steve frowned. "Don't worry about that for now. It won't be easy, but they'll come out okay. We actually have to talk about something a little bit more challenging."

"What do you mean?" I asked, not sure what he was talking about.

"Rolf, they had to give you an ileostomy last night to save your life."

I stared at Steve and Ingrid, a thousand thoughts careening around my brain. *This can't be happening. He must be joking. There's some mistake. Not me.*

I could feel my breathing quicken and my face flush. I stared at my hands resting on the covers. I couldn't believe what I just heard. My life would never be the same. My future had totally changed.

Steve broke the silence for me.

"They didn't tell you before the surgery because they didn't know for sure you would need one. In all honesty, they probably should have done an ostomy nine days ago during the first surgery. I think they made a poor decision, one that unfortunately caused you to go through a lot of suffering and put your life at risk."

I continued to stare off into the distance.

"I'm sure Peskin didn't know exactly what he was going to do until he opened you up again yesterday," Steve continued. "Then he did what he had to do to save your life."

The reality was slowly sinking in.

Steve and Ingrid left at 10 p.m. to go pick up Dad at Lindbergh Field. My father had been traveling for more than twenty-four hours when my brother and sister greeted him at the airport. He'd barely slept in the last two days.

Being home, though, energized him. "It's good to be back," he said, hurrying toward the baggage claim. "So how is Rolf?"

"It's obvious that the second surgery, so soon after the first one, has been awfully tough on his system," Steve answered.

"How are his spirits?"

"He's really down," Ingrid said. "He keeps talking about how hopeless everything is."

"That's not unexpected for what he's gone through," Dad observed. "Remember, Rolf's been fighting this disease for more than a year. I don't think any of us realized how difficult the past twelve months must have been for him. He tried his best to deal with this all by himself and not let us know how much he was hurting. And now, after all this surgery and the assault on his dignity and pride, we have to really try to lift his spirits. None of us can possibly know what it's like to live with an ileostomy. Right now, he's in a day-to-day battle to live."

The reality of what Dad was saying hit Steve and Ingrid. They both nodded in agreement, unable to find words to respond.

They quickly grabbed Dad's bags and hopped into the car for the short drive to the hospital. Dad wanted to check up on me before he headed home, even if I was sleeping. He also wanted to speak with the nurses on duty.

"Hello, Dr. Benirschke," said the night nurse when they arrived at her desk. "Rolf's sleeping. It's the first time he's really slept all day."

"Let him be. I just want to see him for myself." Dad lingered for a moment in the darkened ICU, fighting back tears. Being so far away during this latest trial had been almost impossible to handle, and now that he saw his son hooked up to all the different tubes and machines, the gravity of the situation hit him hard.

Sunday, October 28
8 a.m.

Dad returned to the hospital nine hours later, a little more rested, but anxious to see me.

It was such a relief when I heard his authoritative, full-of-energy voice greet the nurses on duty as he walked into the ICU. "How's my son?" Dad asked. He spent a moment catching up with the nurses and reviewing my chart. Then he gently pulled back the curtain partition and walked over to my bed.

"Hi, Dad. It's great to see you," I whispered through the discomfort of the NG tube stuck in my nose and down my throat.

"The feeling is mutual, Rolf." He had put on a gauze mask to protect me from the cold he had caught while riding airplanes for sixteen hours, but I could still see a smile creep across his face.

Dad gently squeezed my hand, and our eyes met. Within seconds, tears welled up in his eyes. I could count the number of times that I'd ever seen Dad cry. As if a bit ashamed about this emotional display, he turned away from the bed.

"It's okay, Dad."

"I know. Your mother feels very badly that she's not here too, but she needs to be with Opa. I told her you're getting better."

"How is Opa?"

"Not well, but stable. In any event, Mom will be back Thursday."

We talked for a little while about what I had gone through and how his trip went, but I tired quickly. Recognizing that I was fading, Dad urged me to rest and settled into a chair beside my bed to begin reading some of the work he had brought along.

"Dad?" I said, interrupting his concentration a few minutes later.

"Yes?"

"This place is really hard. There always seems to be some emergency going on, and it's hard to even tell whether it's day or night. I feel badly asking for help from the nurses . . . they are swamped."

"Rolf, it's hard for them. They are dealing with really sick people and exposed to so much. Sometimes they almost need to detach themselves just to get by. But don't worry. I'm going to be here all day to catch up on my work and give them a little break."

Dad changed the subject. "Steve is returning to Cleveland tonight. He's got to get back to medical school. Ingrid is home cleaning up and doing laundry, but she will stop by soon."

I recoiled as a wave of pain hit me like a hard punch to the stomach. "Oh, God!" I cried out. "Here we go again." My hands twisted the bed sheet into a ball as I tried to ride out the spasm of pain that seared through my abdomen.

"Easy, Rolf. It's okay. I'm here," Dad said soothingly. "This will pass. It's probably just gas pain."

Drs. Peskin and Griffith, both wearing masks, arrived on rounds shortly before noon. They shook hands with Dad and spent a few minutes examining my chart together. When they moved closer to my bed, Dad spoke in a concerned voice.

"He's in a lot of pain. It seems to come in waves, and when it's there, it's very powerful."

"We'll get him another shot of morphine," Dr. Peskin said.

"Not more morphine," I moaned. I had learned that while morphine cut some of the pain, it also caused me to have weird hallucinations.

"There's no need to be a hero, young man. Small amounts of morphine will help take the edge off the pain." Dr. Peskin looked down and made a notation on my chart.

Dr. Griffith finished his examination. "His lungs are clear, which is a good sign. He also seems to be breathing better."

Dr. Peskin stepped closer. "The spiking fevers are most likely due to pockets of bacteria that are still getting released into your system, especially after you move around or take a walk," he said. Then Dr. Peskin motioned Dad toward the nurses' station. Once there, he spoke softly out of earshot.

"Obviously, the next couple of days are crucial," Dr. Peskin whispered gravely. "He's not home free yet. But if we can weather the next few days without a setback—and can somehow keep Rolf's spirits up—the worst will be behind us."

My father then broached a difficult subject. "Gerald, he keeps talking about how difficult it is to stay here in the ICU."

"Sad to say, he's not the first to comment on that. Unfortunately, he's still way too sick to even consider moving him. Let's see how the next few days go."

When they returned, Dad turned my bed so that we could watch the Sunday NFL games. The Chargers had the day off, having lost to the hated Raiders, 45-22, on Thursday night.

"The Chargers are floundering without you," Dr. Peskin said when he, trying to raise my spirits.

"Thanks, Doc, but I don't think so. The Chargers are doing just fine." I felt sorry for myself. I should be out there on the field with my teammates, but I wasn't. I wondered if I would ever kick in an NFL game again.

Dad turned to Dr. Peskin. "The Chargers have won two games and lost one without Rolf. When he was with them in September, they were three and one. But they have missed him as a kicker, and they're giving a new guy a try today. I can't think of his name."

"Mike Wood," I interrupted, almost smiling. "Dad, I didn't think you followed the Chargers that closely."

"I read the sports page this morning," he said somewhat sheepishly. Dad *never* had time or inclination to read the sports section.

The story was that Roy Gerela, my first replacement, had booted his way out of a job, so the Chargers were giving free agent Mike Wood a shot. Before the loss to the Raiders, he had a good game against the

When I was a rascal, it was hard for my mother, who was pregnant with my sister, Ingrid, to catch me hiding under the table.

My 6th grade class picture taken at Hanover Elementary School in Hanover, New Hampshire.

My father, Kurt, immigrated to the United States from Germany in 1949 with a few dollars in his pocket and a fierce desire to succeed in his adopted country. While working in New York City, he quickly learned English and went on to finish his medical studies at Harvard University. He met my mother, Marion, when she was a nurse at a New Jersey hospital, and they were married in 1952.

Steve, left, is a year-and-a-half older than me, and Ingrid is fourteen months younger. Our formative years were spent enjoying all of the opportunities found at Dartmouth College in the small New England town of Hanover, New Hampshire.

In 1970, Dad was recruited to join the faculty at the University of California San Diego School of Medicine and abruptly moved us across the country to the coastal community of La Jolla, California, just north of San Diego. It was a difficult transition for us kids because we were leaving close friends and the winter sports we enjoyed so much.

Dad loved the new challenges of teaching at the UCSD Medical School and working at University Hospital. Dad's curiosity and interests led him to also get involved with the San Diego Zoo, where he convinced the Zoo board to allow him to set up and run a research center to help better understand their collection of endangered species. Mom adapted well to Southern California and loved the warm weather and winter sunshine.

I was talked into placekicking my senior year at La Jolla High, but because father always stressed the importance of education, I never considered playing sports in college despite strong interest from several big-time Division I football programs. Instead, I decided to pursue my studies in Zoology at the University of California Davis and not play sports. My plans changed when Jim Sochor, the head football coach at UC Davis, talked me into kicking for his team. In a crazy turn of events, I was also recruited to play on the UC Davis soccer team and ended up competing in both sports for three years, even though they took place in the same season.

In the 1977 NFL Draft, I was the next-to-last player picked by the Super Bowl champion Oakland Raiders. I spent all of the preseason with the Raiders and thought I had won the kicking job when a strange set of circumstances sent me to the San Diego Chargers. My sudden move to San Diego was made easier because of Mike Fuller, a great holder who became an even better friend.

There were some long days during my rookie year with the Chargers. We were a young team, and our star quarterback Dan Fouts was holding out. Halfway through the season, I was really struggling when an encouraging letter from a twelve-year-old boy helped me turn things around, and I didn't miss a field goal for the rest of the season.

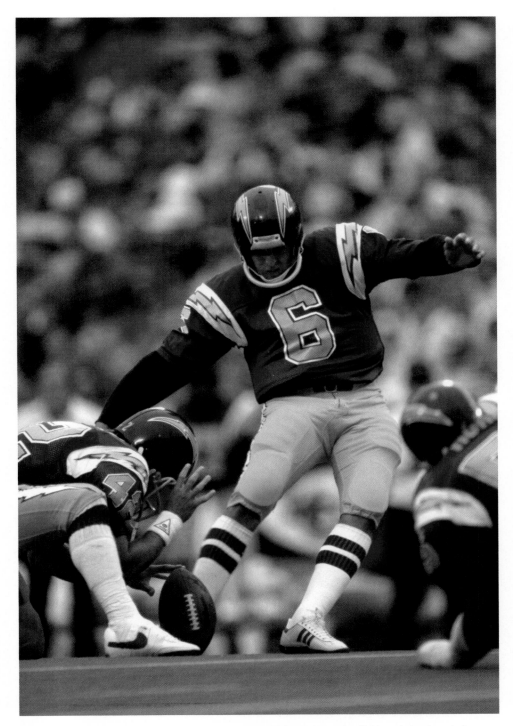

With Mike Fuller's expert holding, I ended up kicking twelve consecutive field goals to close out my rookie year, and I felt like I belonged in the National Football League.

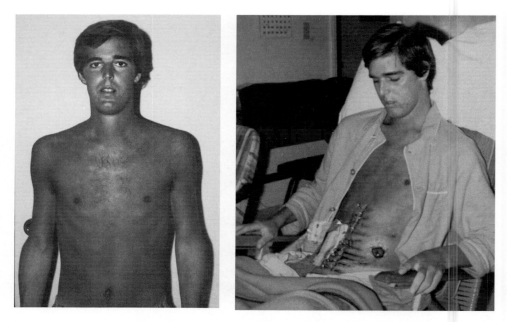

After the success of my rookie year, things changed dramatically when I was diagnosed with Crohn's disease early in my second season. I was in constant pain and struggled to keep weight on, but I continued to play. Everything changed four games into my third season, when I collapsed on a team charter flight returning home from a game. I would need two life-saving surgeries just a few days apart that left me wearing two ostomy bags and my abdomen being held together by painful wire sutures.

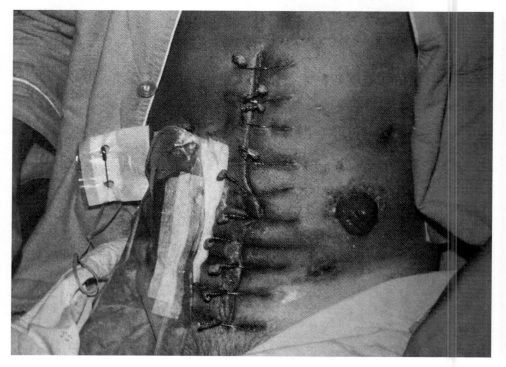

My brother, Steve, interrupted his medical school studies and flew home from Cleveland, Ohio, to help my parents manage the challenging situation we found ourselves in.

While I was in the hospital going through my operations, my sister, Ingrid, was two floors above me undergoing her own surgery to remove a kidney stone.

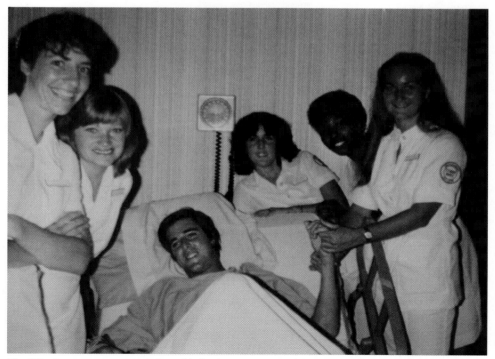

My difficult recovery was made bearable by the great nurses I had at University Hospital in San Diego. I will never forget their kindness, encouragement, and dedication.

Shortly after being released from the hospital, the Chargers invited me to come watch a game and visit my teammates. They surprised me by naming me an honorary captain for the game. I weighed just 123 pounds and could hardly walk to midfield for the coin toss, but I was supported by Louie Kelcher on a day that changed my life and is still remembered by the 52,000 fans in San Diego Stadium that day.

I will forever be indebted to Chargers strength coach Phil Tyne, whose encouragement and support during the long days and months of my recovery made all the difference. It was under his watchful eye that I was able to kick again in the NFL.

Coming back to kick in the NFL again allowed me to deflect the attention focused on me as an athlete to my passion for wildlife and create Kicks for Critters, a program that helped raise money and awareness for the San Diego Zoo's Center for Reproduction of Endangered Species.

In order to get young kids excited to learn about endangered species, we brought school groups to the San Diego Zoo to interact with some special zoo friends.

I was worried about what kinds of activities I might be forced to give up after my ostomy surgery, but I learned that I could do everything I had done prior to my operations, including skiing again.

I felt fortunate that the Chargers gave me a chance to compete for my job again and was excited to kick this game-winning field goal against the Tampa Bay Bucs.

In a game that paralleled my life, I was given a second chance to kick the game-winning field goal in overtime that ended "The Epic in Miami"—a Chargers 41-38 victory over the Miami Dolphins in 1982 that is still considered one of the greatest games in NFL history.

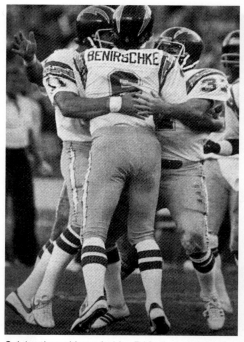

Celebrating with my holder Ed Luther and good friend Hank Bauer.

Mobbed by teammates including our leader, Coach Don Coryell.

Playing in the NFL opened up a lot of interesting opportunities, including an invitation to play in a fund-raising tennis tournament at the White House. On another occasion, I was invited to the White House where I was thrilled to meet President Ronald Reagan and First Lady Nancy Reagan at a dinner reception.

Los Angeles Rams, kicking two field goals and four of five extra points. The Chargers also played well, crushing the Rams, 40-16.

While watching an NFL double-header, late in the second game, I was struggling to keep my eyes open.

"Get some sleep, Rolf," Dad said, noticing my wavering attention. "You need it . . . we all need it."

When I awoke a couple of hours later, I could hear Ingrid and Steve talking with Dad outside the partition. When they heard me stir, they pulled back the curtain.

"Hey, buddy," Steve said. "I wanted to say goodbye before I hopped on the red-eye back to Cleveland tonight. How about one more walk before I go?"

I nodded, and all three of my family members gently helped me out of the bed. Together we shuffled for five minutes down the length of the trauma center and back. After easing me back into bed, I got emotional knowing Steve was leaving.

I looked at my brother through tears of gratitude. "You being here has meant more than I can ever express to you. And I know you made it easier for Mom and Dad, too. Thanks. I hope I didn't cause you to miss too much school."

"It's no big deal. It was kind of like on-the-job training anyway. Besides, I would have been useless trying to study and keep up with my classes while you were going through this. I'm really glad I came."

I smiled and squeezed his hand again.

Dad turned to Steve and Ingrid. "Let's allow Rolf to get some more sleep. And Rolf, Ingrid and I have been invited for dinner tonight by our neighbors—Flo and Wayne Kennedy. We'll stop by after we're done, but we need to leave now as well."

Shortly after they had left, a nurse came in to remove the dressing on my large abdominal incision. The doctor wanted the wound exposed to air several times a day to quicken the healing process so she left my bandages off, intending to come back shortly and replace them. After she left, I gazed at my two ostomy bags, the deep gaping wound of my incision, and the ugly wire sutures holding everything together. Tears of self-pity welled up in my eyes.

As if to make matters worse, I was suddenly seized by shaking chills that were coupled again with a high spiking fever. Because of my open abdominal wound, I couldn't move at all, which meant I was unable to reach the call button or the telephone. I was helpless—like a turtle on its back . . . shaking and freezing cold and burning up all at the same time. I tried calling out for a nurse, but I didn't have the strength to raise my voice. Nobody heard me . . . and nobody came.

I became panicked, frightened that I would begin shaking so violently I would tear out all of my sutures. Fifteen interminable minutes passed before a nurse finally heard my plaintive cries.

"I called out and no one came. Where were you?" There was terror in my voice.

"Sorry," the nurse replied in an icy tone, "but we have a lot of sick people here who need tending to. Besides, I was on dinner break."

On dinner break! What if something worse had happened?

My fever had soared to 104.3, and my resting pulse was up to 150. The nurse became concerned and called for an orderly. They gave me Tylenol and, together, lifted me onto a cool water-filled mattress to try to control my temperature.

At the same time, I felt ice cold and begged for warm blankets. My wound was hastily covered, and I lay there shaking, teeth chattering, as scared and helpless as I'd ever been in my life.

"Please call Dr. Peskin," I pleaded. "And please try to reach my father."

"It's Sunday night," she said matter-of-factly. "I hate to call a doctor on Sunday night. The Tylenol will help."

"Okay, call my father then!"

"We tried, but there's no one home."

Where were he and Ingrid eating dinner?

"Keep trying, please!" I was getting frantic and more scared by the moment. The nurse left to attend to another patient, but matters got worse. I had begun another bout of shaking chills when suddenly something exploded off one of the machines above my head, sounding like a gun had gone off.

I didn't know what had happened, but in my anxious state I figured it had to be serious. I frantically tried getting the nurse's attention, but once again I was unsuccessful. When she finally checked in twenty minutes later, she offered no explanation or words of sympathy.

I implored her to try to reach Dad once more, but it took her nearly an hour to find him. He had just gotten home from dinner when she finally reached him.

Dad and Ingrid wasted no time and got back down to the hospital as quickly as they could. When they finally arrived around 9 p.m., they found me in a state of complete panic. I broke down with relief when they walked in and attempted to explain what had happened.

"It was horrible! These people don't seem to care! Dad, don't leave me alone again, please!" Then I started to sob uncontrollably, even though each inhaled breath caused incredible pain along my incision. I was so relieved to see them that I couldn't control myself any more.

"Rolf, easy. We're here and won't leave you again. Try to relax. You're safe. Take some slow, deep breaths if you can and concentrate on trying to relax your muscles. That's it . . . slow, gentle breaths."

After a few minutes, I settled down and Dad stepped out to the nurses' station to call Dr. Peskin at home.

"He's not doing well, Gerald. He had a bad episode that scared him terribly, and his fever spiked again. It's like he's seen a ghost. He's just now calming down."

"Thanks for calling, Kurt. I'll come down right away," the surgeon assured him. He was a kind man and genuinely cared about his patients.

When Dad came back into my room, I was still pretty distraught.

"Dad, I was terrified and felt so helpless. I couldn't get anyone to hear me or help me! My wound was completely uncovered and when I started the shaking chills, I couldn't move to reach the call button. It was awful." Tears welled up again in my eyes. "I couldn't believe nobody came."

"I guess they're a little short-staffed on the weekends," Dad responded. "From now on, we'll be sure that one of us is here with you—twenty-four hours a day—whenever Carla or Sheana are off duty. We'll put a rotating 'watch team' together so this can't happen again."

Dr. Peskin arrived at the Trauma Unit at 9:30 p.m. He examined my chart, asked a few questions, and quickly ordered two more units of blood. After a quick check and irrigation of the surgical opening, he announced, "The good news is that the ileostomy is working. The bad news is we still haven't gotten the bacteria in your system under control." He called the head of the infectious disease team at home, and together they decided to be more aggressive with their use of different antibiotics.

Nurse Carla van den Hour arrived for the 10 p.m. shift, which gladdened Ingrid.

"Thank God, you're here," my sister said. "Rolf had a really difficult time tonight when we were gone. He's frightened and needs to have someone here that he has confidence in. You're one of the few people he feels really safe with."

"Poor guy," Carla responded. "He's going through a lot right now."

"Yes, he sure is."

With Carla there, I fell asleep pretty quickly. Ingrid and Dad decided to head home to get some sleep themselves.

MONDAY, OCTOBER 29
5:30 A.M.

The phone rang at the nurses' station.

"Hello, Carla, this is Dr. Benirschke. I've been up half the night, worrying about Rolf."

Nurse Carla didn't sugarcoat her report. "I'm afraid your son had a difficult night, Dr. Benirschke. He hardly slept, and when he did, he was hallucinating and having terrible nightmares. Probably a reaction to the morphine. I've already notified Dr. Peskin, but we're all still very concerned."

"I'll be right there." Dad hung up the phone quickly.

When my father arrived, I was having another terrible chill, and my temperature was again a boiling 104 degrees. Although I was well-covered by blankets, I felt as cold as ice. My teeth chattered violently.

"I can't stop shaking, Dad. I can't stop no matter how hard I try. Is this what it's like before you die?"

My father looked into the distance. I could tell he was weighing his words, so I spoke first.

"I'm dying, Dad. I know it. You know it. They all know it."

"Rolf, stop talking like that," Dad interrupted. "You are not dying. Your fever should break shortly. It's just the body's way of fighting the infection."

But an hour later, the chills were still persisting. "This is unbelievably awful," I mumbled, hardly coherent. "It's like something is tearing me up inside." My hands were clenched tightly, my teeth were chattering, and my body was still shaking visibly.

"Dad?"

"Yes, son?"

"I'm really scared."

I paused and squeezed my eyes shut, then opened them and looked at my father.

"Will you promise me one thing, Dad?"

"Yes. Whatever you want."

"Promise me that you won't let them keep me alive if there is no hope."

A long, agonizing pause came between us.

"I promise . . . I won't let them keep you alive."

"Thanks, Dad."

My father blinked away a couple of tears, then turned away. He didn't want me to see him crying.

Ingrid arrived at noon, and Dad left my side for the first time in nearly six hours. In the hallway outside the Trauma Unit, he found Bob Ortman, a longtime sportswriter for the *San Diego Evening Tribune*.

Mr. Ortman, who had covered the Chargers since they began playing in San Diego in 1961, had been stopping by University Hospital nearly every day since my first surgery. He was never allowed into the Trauma Unit to see me, but he was able to pick up information about my condition from a passing nurse or my father. He also faithfully wrote me little notes of encouragement every day, but on this afternoon, the look on Dad's face told him it was Kurt Benirschke who needed support.

"I hear he's in rough shape," Mr. Ortman said gently.

Dad couldn't answer. All the pressure of the last two weeks finally got the best of my father, and he began to sob big, heaving cries. The gentle-hearted, crusty old sportswriter didn't hesitate and quietly wrapped his arms around Dad and let him cry. It was several minutes before Dad could speak. Two grown men hanging onto each other connected over the concern of a young man they both cared for.

"He just made me promise that I wouldn't keep him alive if it came down to artificial means, or if I thought he was terminal," Dad confided. "I'm afraid he's losing his will to live."

Ortman continued to comfort Dad, and together they held each other up until the sportswriter had to go twenty minutes later.

Over the next few hours, Dr. Peskin visited me several times. He knew he had to stay ahead of the changing bacteria so he switched antibiotics again, changed my dressing, and irrigated the surgical wound.

Then some good news: My fever finally broke in mid-afternoon, dropping to 100.2, and for the first time in twenty-four hours, my body relaxed. The ordeal, however, had left me exhausted and completely spent.

Dad, who had regrouped, took the opportunity to bolster my spirits. "I don't know if you're aware of it, but a whole bunch of people are donating blood for you through a small blood drive organized by your good friend, John Grantham, and the radio station that carries the Chargers games."

"There are a lot of people pulling for you, Rolf," Ingrid added. "Everywhere I go, I run into folks who ask about you and how you're doing. It's got to make you feel great to have so many people behind you."

Before I could answer, Dr. Peskin arrived on his rounds. He motioned for Dad and Ingrid to join him in the hallway outside the ICU.

"I know it's always dangerous to speculate on these things," the surgeon said, "but I have good feelings about what happened here this afternoon."

"That *would* be wonderful," my dad said. His face was drawn and sunken from too many days with too little sleep.

"I know it's been a rough couple of weeks," the surgeon continued, "but I think we've finally found the right combination of antibiotics. His white blood cell count is beginning to drop noticeably, and it appears we're finally getting ahead of the infection."

Still Going Strong

The Chargers Blood Drive that was spontaneously put together during my hospitalization has grown into an annual event that's always held on the Tuesday before Thanksgiving and is San Diego's longest running and most successful blood drive every year. In fact, the Chargers Blood Drive became the nation's largest single-day collection and is in the Guinness Book of World Records.

In 2014, Chargers Blood Drive XXXVI—using Roman numbers like the Super Bowl—drew more than 2,000 donors. Chargers players, alumni, and the Charger Girls were on hand for pictures and autographs while musical acts of all kinds entertained the thousands of fans in attendance.

In addition, every radio station in town broadcasts live from the Town & Country Convention Center in Mission Valley, the site of the Blood Drive each year. The blood drive also has a Wellness Zone, where fans can get their blood pressure, cholesterol, blood sugar levels, and other important health markers checked.

It's hard to believe that a small grassroots blood drive, created to help save my life and restore almost 80 units I needed during my two surgeries, has grown into such a special event that draws the community together every year . . . and has for more than thirty-six years!

My father and sister each breathed a sigh a relief. When they finally returned home later that night, they were emotionally whipped after the wild roller coaster day. But they also felt upbeat, and for the first time in days, they actually got a good night's sleep.

I didn't rest as well.

I may have been alive, but as I looked again at the bags attached to my side, I wondered if my life was really worth saving.

10

RETURN TO SENDER

I was just waking up after a groggy night of sleep when Jim Adkins stopped in. The youth pastor lifted my spirits immediately. He wasn't there ten minutes, however, when an officious hospital administrator in his early thirties interrupted us. He held a clipboard in his hands.

"Mr. Benirschke?"

"Yes," I replied.

"Mr. Benirschke, if you have a moment, I need to go over some things with you."

"Go ahead."

"It seems that your insurance company has not been responsive, so we've had to turn your account over to a collection agency. The amount is in excess of $20,000." (In today's dollars, that amount would be nearly $70,000.)

"What are you talking about?" I asked, completely stunned. "Look at me. I just had surgery a few days ago. I'm not going anywhere, and you're coming in here asking for money? Forgive me for being a little upset, but just for your information, I'm covered under the Chargers' team insurance and my dad happens to work here. It's not like you won't be able to find me." I couldn't believe what was happening.

"Ah, no, I wasn't aware of that," fumbled the administrator. "There must be some mistake here. Perhaps I can go back to my office to straighten it out . . . ."

With that, he turned on his heels and left the ICU.

"Wow, Jim. It's like I'm not a person at all—just a bill to be collected on."

"Easy, Rolf. There has to be some kind of explanation."

Just then Dad and Ingrid walked in, and Jim replayed what had just taken place.

"It really was unbelievable," Jim said. "I can't understand what they were thinking."

Dad looked bewildered. He was embarrassed for the behavior of the hospital that he was so proud to work for, and to have that interchange happen to a family member really upset him. "I'll take care of this, son. Don't worry about it one minute more."

With that, Dad strode over to the nurses' station and called downstairs to University Hospital's administrative offices.

"This is Dr. Benirschke," he said, his right hand cupped over the receiver. "You will have to excuse me for being a little upset, but rather astonishingly, my son, who is in the Trauma Unit and is recovering from a second major surgery four days ago, has just been told that his hospital bill has been turned over to a collection agency!"

The excuse—that it was the bill for the anesthesia from my first surgery and that the departments bill separately—didn't hold much water for Dad. I could almost hear the backpedaling, and when Dad came back to my bed, I knew that was the last time we would be bothered.

"They recognize this matter should have been handled differently, and that it was an extremely insensitive thing to do under any circumstances," Dad said. But he couldn't hide a faint smile as he spoke. To a doctor, he knew my righteous anger was indicative of one thing: I was getting better.

What Are the Insurance Implications Today for Ostomy Surgery?

Ostomy surgery is always covered by all forms of health insurance, even by the Affordable Care Act, otherwise generally known as Obamacare.

Ostomy surgery is a "standard of care" procedure for many diseases, including inflammatory bowel disease, rectal cancer, bladder cancer, and for wounds and internal injuries that may damage the digestive tract.

WEDNESDAY, OCTOBER 31

8:45 A.M.

I awoke with Dad's secretary, Mary Byrd, sitting in a chair at the foot of my bed. Mary was one of a half-dozen friends who volunteered to maintain an around-the-clock vigil after my bad night five days earlier. Waking up to her pleasant smile bolstered my spirits, and it was the best I'd felt in weeks. When Dad dropped by after breakfast, he noticed the difference right away.

"That secretary of yours is really special," I grinned.

"I know," he replied. "After what happened, we're just not going to take any more chances. I'm afraid the nursing service is just under-staffed."

Until now, my preoccupation had been on surviving, but now I needed to begin dealing with the outcome of my surgery. On this morning, I would receive my first ileostomy lesson. Melba Conner, a WOC (wound, ostomy, and continence) nurse, was scheduled to come in and teach me how my appliance worked.

Naturally, I felt apprehensive and skeptical. But Melba had an ileostomy of her own, and out of that experience she had become one of the first WOC nurses in the country. When she told me of her own experiences and that she had helped more stoma patients than anyone, she quickly gained my trust and got my full attention. She talked openly about living with an appliance, what I could expect, and how little my lifestyle would actually change.

I still wasn't convinced that I could lead a normal life, however. "I don't know, Melba. I'm not sure I can handle all of this," I confessed with skepticism.

"It's not a question of whether or not you can handle it," she replied firmly. "There is simply no option. Besides, if it weren't for the surgery, you'd be six feet under right now, and you wouldn't have any choice at all."

I stared at her. She had my attention now.

"I know this is a huge change for anybody, and maybe more so for someone as athletic as you. Listen, I don't follow football much, but I've never heard the nurses talk about a patient getting so much mail before. You must have a lot of support out there, so if I were you, I'd start by being thankful for my blessings."

Melba removed my appliance and touched my stoma with her gloved index finger. "Now, let's get to the basics. It's going to seem overwhelming at first, but for now, just watch what I do."

I shook my head and closed my eyes as they started to tear up. *If only those bags would disappear.*

"Look, Rolf," she said, as if she was reading my mind. "These appliances are not going away, and you must learn how they work. For the rest of your life, you're going to have to do this. If you learn well, they shouldn't interfere with anything you do."

Melba took my hand and had me touch my left stoma. It was shiny, a bit wet-looking, and dark pink—not unlike the lining of the mouth. The one-inch round stoma protruded from my side about half an inch.

Melba explained that there were no nerve endings in the stoma, so touching it couldn't hurt. The stoma's redness meant it was well vascularized, she said, adding that I may notice a little blood every now and then—perfectly natural and no cause for alarm—when changing the appliance.

"You're lucky to have had your surgery now," she said. "Modern appliances allow you to go from four to six days before changing pouches, and they shouldn't leak or smell. You will have to empty your bag a number of times during the day, depending on how much you eat or drink, but that will become routine very quickly. Remember, it wasn't so long ago that only primitive appliances were available and some patients would fashion their own, using everything from pasted-on receptacles to old rubber water bottles or plastic bags with gauze or paper to absorb the effluent. They would almost always leak and smell, and the corrosion on the patient's skin was absolutely horrendous."

"Maybe I am fortunate." I spoke with a little optimism . . . the first positive thought I'd uttered in a while.

"You are," she reminded me. "Now let's change those bags of yours."

Melba gently removed my old appliances and cleaned around the stomas with soap and water. She was careful not to snag anything on my protruding wire sutures or touch my painful incision. Then she patted the area dry with a towel and used an alcohol swab to wipe the area around the stomas.

Next, she cut two stoma-sized holes out of a pair of faceplate barriers that would snugly fit around the stomas to protect my skin from the corrosive digestive enzymes that exist in the intestines. Before she attached them, however, she spread a whitish paste on the skin around my stomas and waited several minutes for the glue to get tacky.

Big Improvements

The technology behind appliances has changed dramatically in thirty-five years. Today, patients no longer need to apply paste of any kind, and the appliances can be changed in a matter of seconds. There are different options: one- or two-piece, open- or closed-ended, and they can still be worn from four to seven days, depending on your activity level.

Perhaps most importantly, the appliances rarely leak and do not smell at all. Most are so low profile that nobody will know you have one on unless you tell them.

With the gentleness of someone who had done this thousands of times, she carefully fitted the face plates over my stomas one at a time and gently pressed them securely onto my abdomen. After adding paper tape around the face plate borders, she attached the new pouches, which snapped into a secure position much like a Tupperware lid. Voila! I had new appliances, and the whole process took only ten minutes.

Melba checked the clip on the bag collecting the waste. "When you're up and around, you'll need to empty your pouch six or seven times a day," she said. "You'll learn very quickly how your digestive system works and when your bag is full."

"What about the odor?"

"Not a problem. The new appliances prevent that. Naturally, there's an odor when you empty your pouch in the bathroom, but that shouldn't be any different from any normal bowel movement."

"How do I empty the pouch?" I asked, still a little overwhelmed.

"Let's wait a couple of hours on that, and then I'll show you how it's done."

Later that morning, Melba led me to the bathroom and asked me to sit on the toilet. "What you do is take the pouch and drain it between your legs."

I disrobed and did as she ordered.

"Now, undo the clip and drain the contents right into the bowl."

Melba, bless her heart, stayed with me as I clumsily unclipped the pouch and poured the smelly contents into the toilet bowl.

"Now take some tissue and clean the end of the bag before you put the clip back on," she instructed.

She coached me every step of the way and made everything seem relatively simple and effortless. Then Melba accompanied me back to my bed, where I laid down and wondered whether I'd ever be able to change and empty my appliance so easily on my own.

"Any more questions?" she asked, interrupting my thoughts.

"No. The toughest part is still accepting this. It's not an easy thing to look at."

A firm look returned to Melba's face, but then it softened. "Don't worry," she soothed. "You're going to do just fine. There may even be a day when you will look back and count this among your many blessings. Life has a funny way of getting our attention and teaching us what's really important when we least expect it."

No Resistance

The wire sutures in my abdomen were hurting, and I felt more like a pin cushion than a person. For the last few weeks, my body had been cut and poked and squeezed and shaken in more ways than I thought possible. Doctors and nurses came in and did whatever they wanted whenever they wanted . . . and there was little I could do about it.

That afternoon, I was helped out of bed twice for walks around the room. Despite the activity, my fever did not rise. *Finally, a good sign,* I thought. Until now, I had come to associate walks with shaking chills and rising fevers that ensued immediately afterward. Those events caused me to not want to take walks.

Five days after the surgery, the hospital's Infectious Disease department was beginning to win the battle against my massive infection, and there was a noticeable change in my outlook. Because of my improving condition, Dr. Peskin said I could begin taking food orally for the first time since my second operation, as long as I felt up to it.

In the meantime, the get-well cards continued to be delivered by the bagful. The thought of so many Chargers fans taking the time to sit down and write me a letter of encouragement humbled me. I imagined that most people suffering from these diseases struggled alone, or with just a few close family members or friends aware of what they were going through.

I felt undeserving of the attention.

Support Through Social Media

Steve Jobs and Steve Wozniak were just trying to get a small start-up company called Apple off the ground in 1979, so the digital revolution was still a couple of decades away. Today, easy access to smartphones and social media means that your friends and family can reach out to you and encourage you, practically in real time.

Is this a good thing? Of course. But I can tell you that I will never forget the people who took the time to actually come to the hospital and visit me or sat down to write me a note. I was never able to thank the hundreds of people personally although I tried.

Today with social media, there seems to be a desire to share everything that goes on in a person's life. While this can be fun and interesting, ostomy surgery is a life-changing event and a big deal. It takes time to come to grips with the experience—emotionally, physically, and spiritually—as well as all of the repercussions of what this surgery entails from a lifestyle point of view.

So yes, I would encourage you to share what's happening with your online friends and family, but don't feel pressured to reveal everything in social media until you're ready to do so. People take their cues from you . . . if you feel comfortable with your situation, they are more likely to feel that way as well.

Meanwhile, Ingrid had been reading through some of the letters the nurse had just delivered.

"Rolf, listen to this," she said.

> I'm a twenty-year-old guy, and I had the same surgery you did. In a matter of just two months, I went from being in seemingly perfect health to getting diagnosed with a disease and having an ostomy, a type of operation I had never even heard of before.
>
> The experience made me realize just how fragile life can be. But it also taught me about how resilient and adaptable the human body is. While feeling sorry for myself after surgery, my father sympathetically pointed out that there were a lot of people worse off than me, and all I had to do was look around at other patients in the hospital to realize that. I soon knew he was absolutely right.
>
> My condition suddenly seemed minor compared to others I saw. I treat life and health with much more respect now than before my illness, but the desire to experience life to the fullest is stronger than it's ever been. I know you're probably going through a rough time right now, but I just want you to know that my thoughts are with you. I'm hoping that by hearing my story that you will be encouraged to get back at it. We miss you on the field.

"Wow!" I said. "What a neat letter."

"I thought so, too. Here's another," said Ingrid.

> You're not alone. I have suffered with IBD for more than ten years. The worst came seven years ago when my small bowel perforated, requiring three operations within two weeks. Rather than reconnect my intestines, my doctor decided I needed an ostomy.

Those next two months in bed were very difficult. I'll never forget the first step I took on my sixty-first day, just before passing out. My strength comes from my music. The nurses would help me to the hospital piano—wheelchair, tubes, and all—where I could play with whatever energy I had left. Slowly, each day, I noticed I could play a little longer. At that point, I knew my recovery was heading in the right direction, even though I was only 120 pounds.

Since then, my wife and I have had two beautiful children, and I have a good job. I have always liked the challenge of mountain climbing and thought I might not be able to do it again. But that's not the case. During my many climbs since my operation, I have had to face storms, cold, darkness, mountain walls, ice, snow, getting lost, and running out of water at 14,000 feet. But my desire to really "live life" has never been greater. It means more to me now than ever. My ostomy surgery saved my life and gave me the chance to return to what I love to do.

"Is that remarkable or what?" Ingrid asked incredulously. "A mountain climber with an ostomy."

I tried my best to gulp down the lump in my throat. "It's pretty amazing," I agreed. "I'm having a hard time climbing out of bed. The thought of climbing a mountain seems pretty near impossible to me right now . . . especially wearing a bag."

It was amazing to me that I was receiving so many letters because my ostomy surgery had not been publicly announced. The newspapers and local TV news were busy reporting that I had Crohn's disease and had undergone surgery, but that was as far as the stories went. From the letters I was receiving, though, it was clear that people familiar with the illness recognized that I had likely undergone an ileostomy procedure as well.

I closed my eyes and thought of the many walks I had taken around the hospital corridors. At least I could still stand on my own two legs. I remembered the woman in 11D with the spinal-cord injury; she would never walk again. I remembered seeing the man without arms and legs in 11J, and next door were several patients in oxygen tents with their mouths open and their eyes shut.

Melba was right; I had been feeling sorry for myself. There were people right around me, right on this floor, who were much worse off than me. I needed to quit whining.

Ingrid interrupted my thoughts. "The entire mail sack is filled with encouraging letters like this. And this is only the start of it. The Chargers are going to bring a couple more bags of mail over to the house tomorrow."

"Ingrid, how am I going to answer all of these people?"

My sister smiled. She knew that none of these people expected an answer; they just wanted me to know they cared and were pulling for me.

Simply, that they were thinking of me. That was all. I was deeply, deeply moved and humbled by their kindness.

Thursday, November 1
6:30 a.m.

I awoke early to find Mary Byrd reading a book under a small lamp. She had been by my side all night . . . again.

"Mary, it's so great to have you here," I whispered.

She looked up from her book and grinned. "It's nice to see you finally get some sleep. Besides, now I can tell everyone I spent the night with a handsome Chargers hero."

I laughed, but then I realized that it had been a long time since I had thought about girls. I had been dating my college girlfriend, Kris, fairly steadily since my sophomore year in college, but our relationship had been growing apart for more than a year, partly because she lived in Los Angeles, and partly because we were both still maturing. Although we had begun to go our separate ways, Kris had kindly called Mom and Dad to find out how I was on several occasions.

The hospital dietician came by at 8 o'clock and interrupted my thoughts. "Dr. Peskin says you can start eating some regular food," she announced. "Any special requests?"

"Yeah. Scrambled eggs and toast for breakfast. And how about a hamburger and fries for lunch?" I licked my lips with anticipation.

"C'mon, now. Within reason."

"Well, actually, I have this terrible craving for cherry popsicles. Do you think I'm pregnant?" I felt good enough to make a joke.

"I don't know about the pregnant part, but cherry popsicles we can handle. More importantly, popsicles are something your tummy can handle. I also think we can wrestle up some good ol' chicken noodle soup."

"To tell you the truth, it's been so long since I've even thought about food. I've almost forgotten what it tastes like."

Mary Byrd knew how much I loved Italian food. "Tell you what," she said. "When you're ready, I promise I'll bring you a pepperoni pizza or spaghetti Bolognese."

At noon, Dad and Carla helped me out of bed for a walk around the room. But the effort quickly exhausted me, and I needed to rest in a nearby chair. As I sat, I was suddenly overcome by the enormity of my situation. I was so weak and frail.

"That was nothing more than a simple walk around the room. So why did it wipe me out?" I bemoaned.

Dad looked at me, and I could see his shoulders sag.

"Obviously, your body is still recovering from the operations," he answered. "You've lost over sixty pounds and need to learn to be a little more patient and not expect too much too soon."

Dr. Peskin arrived just then and announced he wanted to start pulling out the drains in my abdomen. "Not all the way out, but part way to see how your body handles it," he said.

Dr. Peskin had told me the day before that he was going to start to do this, but he promised it wouldn't hurt. They always tell you that when you're in the hospital.

The four drains, which had been placed around the incision, were about six inches long. They looked like flat balloons and were about half-an-inch wide. They needed to be pulled out one inch a day. There was only a moment of real pain as each drain was tugged, but the apprehension was murder.

Encouragingly, there appeared to be no pus or other signs of infection. But ten minutes later, after Dr. Peskin had left the room to continue his rounds, I had a fever spike to an alarming 103.5, and the frightening chills returned as well.

Ingrid quickly left my room to try to find a doctor.

Dr. Peskin quickly answered his pager and came racing back to the Trauma Unit. After looking me over, he said reassuringly, "I don't believe there's any reason to panic. Moving the drains has probably seeded some bacteria into your bloodstream, but I anticipate your fever will subside pretty quickly and things will return to normal. This is just the body's way of fighting the infection. It's actually a good sign."

The doctor was calm and comforting, and, as always, I felt better after he visited. Dr. Peskin sensed that, and he made it a point to stop in as often as he could.

To help calm me down, he ordered Valium and Tylenol and then told Dr. Griffith that the Foley catheter could also be removed once I settled down a bit. Then some good news: the fever broke about forty-five minutes later.

The "Rolf Watch" continued with Dad succeeding Ingrid and Jim Adkins succeeding Dad. At midnight, when Nurse Carla came on duty, my temperature was a stable 99 and my pulse was 88. I slept through the night.

When Cammy Mowery came on her rounds early Friday morning, she had me try the blow bottle.

"Excellent," the intern pronounced. "Your lungs are clearing, and, except for the one fever spike yesterday when Dr. Peskin moved the drains, we've kept your fever under control for more than forty-eight hours."

"Is that really that big a deal?" I asked.

"It may not sound like much to the outside world, but in your situation, it's very significant. We still need you to get out of bed three or four times every day and to keep expanding your lungs by using the blow bottles. You've got to keep pushing yourself."

I had been getting out of my bed and walking at least that much, so I felt I was doing what the doctor ordered. I took two more walks with Ingrid and Sheana. Although there were no more fever spikes that day, I lay tensely in bed after each walk, expecting the worst.

The only discouraging sign was that my white blood count, which had risen to 21,300, indicated the infection still wasn't under control. There was nothing more I could do except wait.

To help distract me, Ingrid opened more mail.

I was touched to learn that a church had put my name in the Sunday bulletin asking for prayer, and another congregation was circulating my name in their prayer chain.

Ingrid read two more letters aloud before noticing that I was nodding off. She put the notes down and said, "Get some sleep. Mom gets back tonight, and I know she'll be anxious to see you. Save some energy for her."

I nodded before dozing off. I thought my most difficult days were behind me, but none of us could have been prepared for what was to happen next.

11

Things Happen in Threes

Dad dropped by my room in time to watch the Chargers' game with me on a rare Thursday night edition of *Monday Night Football*. After examining my charts, he settled into his now-familiar chair for a relaxed evening of football.

Just before the opening kickoff, the announcers were discussing the key matchups when the camera suddenly panned to the Chargers bench. There, holding a homemade sign, was equipment manager Doc Brooks and several Chargers players.

The camera zoomed in, and as I made out the words, goose bumps came over me. The sign read:

**Get Well Soon, Rolf
We Need You!**

The makeshift sign completely surprised us, and my father and I watched in silence as Howard Cosell, the enigmatic ABC announcer, provided the verbal caption to the touching scene.

"He's an exemplary young man," said Cosell in his purposeful tone of voice, "and all of us here at ABC join together in wishing him a rapid and complete recovery." By this time Dad and I both had tears in our eyes at the kindness shown by Doc and my teammates. It took several minutes before we could finally speak again.

Lying in my bed, I understood in a real way that I would probably never kick a football again. I had no idea what Cosell's comments meant to the tens of millions of football fans watching the game that evening, but to an emaciated patient in UC San Diego's University Hospital, they would never be forgotten.

After the game, Dad prepared to leave for the airport to pick up Mom.

"I'm sorry Mom wasn't here to see the game, but I'll fill her in," he said. "Actually, maybe it's better she missed seeing that sign. You know how she cries at these things. By the time I pick her up at the airport, it'll be too late to bring her by the hospital, but I'm sure she'll want to see you first thing in the morning."

I nodded in agreement. I was already fading from the emotional evening and looking forward to a good night of sleep. Things had been going so well that we had decided to forego the all-night bedside vigils carried out by those on the "Rolf Watch." It would be my first night alone in days, but it felt good not to be a burden on everybody.

Shortly after Dad left, two nurses arrived to get me out of bed for a brief walk.

"Do I have to?" I asked plaintively. "It's late, and I'm really tired."

Secretly, I still feared the fever and shaking chills that had followed so many of my previous laps around the hospital halls.

"The doctors say you should be getting up four to six times a day now," one of the nurses reminded me. "They also say it's important for you to walk just before bedtime."

Flanked by the two nurses, I trudged to the end of the Trauma Unit and back . . . and did it a second time. When I was done, they helped me back into bed, where I turned on the television set again, this time to watch a rerun of one of my favorite shows, *M*A*S*H*. This had become my routine: walk, climb back into bed around 11 p.m., and turn on *M*A*S*H*. On this evening, things didn't feel quite right. I knew that the nurse would be coming in with a thermometer to check my temperature and see if the shakes would return.

Tonight, it was Carla.

"It's happening again, Carla!" I moaned as I began to shake. "The evening nurses insisted I get out of bed, and now I've spiked a fever. When is this all going to stop?"

Coupled with a soaring temperature, my body began trembling again. I shook with an indescribable chill. Even though I knew better, I blamed the nurses for insisting that I walk.

I shivered under the covers, trying to stay warm. Carla gave me Tylenol, applied cold compresses to my forehead, and sat with me for almost an hour until the fever finally broke and the shakes subsided.

Sheana relieved Carla in the morning, and when she brought my breakfast—oatmeal, milk, dry toast, and canned peaches—I refused to eat. I had no appetite! I tried, but the best I could do was nibble on a piece of bread and a few saltine crackers. Although I had begun eating solid foods several days earlier, it was still a struggle.

When Mom arrived with Dad just after 8 a.m., she expected to see a happy, much-improved son.

"Rolfie! How are you?" Mom gently hugged me and stroked my hair. "I missed you so much."

When she cupped my face in her hands and pulled away to take her first good look at her youngest son, she saw tears in my eyes.

"Honey, what's the matter?"

"I'm not getting any better, Mom. They got me out of bed last night after Dad left, and my temperature went crazy *again*. There just doesn't seem to be an end to all of this. I'm worn out, and it's so discouraging. I was hoping we had finally turned the corner, but now I don't know."

"Now, Rolf," Dad interrupted, a little frustrated at my "poor me" attitude. "You *are* getting better. Everything is pointing in the right direction. You've just got to keep fighting."

OUT OF THE BLUE

Later that morning, after catching up with Mom and hearing how Opa was doing, I began experiencing cramps in the lower left quadrant of my abdomen. This pain felt different from anything I had felt before, and that worried me.

I told Sheana, and she called Dr. Peskin. After reviewing the charts and pondering the problem, Dr. Peskin felt there was a strong possibility that an abscess might have formed, which could also explain the recent fever spikes.

Dr. Peskin quickly ordered an ultrasound to see if they could see anything unusual. Sure enough, the ultrasound revealed what appeared to be a walled-off pocket of pus on my lower left side.

Dr. Griffith came to see me before noon. He had been given the unpleasant task of informing his sick patient about the finding. Dr. Griffith wasn't quite sure how to begin, so he went for the direct approach. He had learned that the best way to handle me was to be upfront and honest.

"After reviewing the ultrasound results, Rolf, it looks as if we've located an abscess that needs to be drained right away. The abscess may be the reason you're still spiking fevers. The only way we can drain it is to take you back to surgery one more time. We've scheduled you for 3 o'clock this afternoon."

This afternoon? Are you kidding me?

As those last words hung in the air, Dr. Griffith saw me close my eyes, clench my teeth, and turn away. *This couldn't be happening to me,* I thought. *Not again.*

I didn't believe I could handle another operation. I was on empty. I was done—through. There was nothing left in the tank. Eighteen months of fighting the disease had taken its toll. The countless number of painful tests, the two major surgeries, multiple IVs, needle sticks, blow bottles—I was running on fumes. I didn't want to give up, but I didn't think there was any way I could mentally get myself up for another operation . . . especially one in just a few hours.

Mom got out of her chair and gently squeezed my hand, sensing the intensity of the moment. What a horrible homecoming for her. She stroked my forehead while deep sobs shook my body.

Having made his announcement, Dr. Griffith quietly slipped out of the room, leaving Mom and me to process what he had just said. A full five minutes passed before I could even try to speak.

"I can't go through it again, Mom. I just can't. I don't think I'll survive another surgery. I just know it."

Mom's response was to squeeze my hands even tighter. If I had looked at her, I would have seen tears in her eyes, too. Her voice, how-ever, never wavered. "Rolf, if another operation is what it's going to take, we'll get through that, too."

I lay there, staring at the clock as the nurses prepped me for one more trip to the operating room. I found myself praying, not with my mind, but from deep within my soul. I explained to God that I had done all I could, and if now was the time to die, I was ready to go. *Lord, I don't believe I can survive another surgery*, I prayed. *If now is the time, okay. It's all in your hands, and I'm ready.* A great peace settled over me as I handed my future over to Him.

Before I was wheeled down to the operating bay, Dr. Griffith manually examined my abdomen again. Strangely, the extreme tenderness seemed to have lessened. As he probed further, he wondered if he had missed something, or if the spot he had seen on the film wasn't an abscess after all.

Dr. Griffith decided to order another ultrasound, just to be sure. Using a pen, he marked the spot on my abdomen where the tenderness had been earlier that morning. If he was correct, the X-rays would show the abscess and confirm where he would make the incision.

On the way to Radiology, I showed little or no emotion. I felt like I was out of my body, looking down on what was happening. What I was going through was completely out of my control, and I felt content, almost peaceful.

I recognized the Radiology nurse, who tried to act cheerful as she and an orderly gently assisted me onto the X-ray table. She applied a cold sonography gel to my abdomen and then rolled a transducer across my midsection. Strangely, nothing appeared on the monitor. The more she looked, the more curious she became.

"Dr. Griffith," the nurse asked quizzically, "we are looking for an abscess, right?"

"Yes, I felt one this morning, and we both saw it on the last ultra-sound."

"It was on the left side, wasn't it?"

"Yes, that's why I marked it."

The nurse continued to explore my abdomen, but she found nothing.

After ten minutes, Dr. Griffith asked the nurse if they could talk for a minute.

They walked over to a corner of the room.

"There doesn't appear to be anything there," she whispered, a little confused.

"You're right," Dr. Griffith said. "According to the sonography from this morning, there should have been a mass showing. But whatever was there before is definitely *not* there now. I don't understand this at all."

After several more minutes of hushed discussion, Dr. Griffith turned to me, somewhat embarrassed. "Young man, it looks as if we've made a mistake," he said. "You don't appear to have an abscess after all. We're going to cancel surgery."

Was I dreaming? No surgery! Relief like I've never experienced before flooded my body. I closed my eyes and uttered a silent prayer of thanksgiving, believing that God had somehow answered my plea and spared me.

Dr. Peskin arrived a few moments after I was brought back to my room with a wry smile on his face. "The only thing we can figure," he tried to explain, "was that we must have been seeing a small gas pocket rather than a fluid mass. When Dr. Griffith examined you manually, the intestine could have shifted and caused you to expel the gas. In any event, since we can't see anything, there's no reason to go into surgery."

That statement didn't sound completely plausible to me, but perhaps the doctors needed an explanation for themselves. For me, I was convinced that God had divinely intervened, perhaps knowing I wasn't capable of surviving another surgery.

Dr. Peskin paused. "Now for some more good news. Since your blood gases have been stabilizing, we won't need to do any more arterial blood draws. I'm also going to have the hyperalimentation discontinued, which will make it a lot easier for you to take your walks. The fact is, your ileostomy is functioning beautifully with the solid foods you've been getting. Some bacteria in your system may still slip into your bloodstream when you exercise, but it should be downhill from here. Believe me, Rolf, we want to get you out of the

ICU and onto a regular floor as soon as possible. Things seem to finally be heading in the right direction."

SPIRITS IMPROVING

Sure enough, I made slow but steady progress over the next two days. My temperature never rose higher than 100.9 on Friday, and it remained unchanged on Saturday.

After Dr. Mowery visited me, she wrote on my chart: "Appetite is improving, along with spirits and attitude. Lungs clear."

On Saturday, Mom and I watched some college football games on TV. During the commercial breaks, she would pick a handful of letters from the mailbag and read them out loud to me. She shook her head after each kind note and finally set a handful on her lap. "I must tell you something, Rolfie," she said, looking up. "These are incredibly touching notes and seem to have done a lot to help lift your spirits. You look 100 percent better tonight than a couple of days ago."

"They really do touch me . . . and I do seem to feel better," I answered. "Or at least I do until I look down and see my bags."

"We can't worry about those now. We need to be concentrating on trying to get out of this hospital and getting you back on your feet. Once we're home, we'll worry about the bags. Remember, it takes lots of little steps to climb a mountain, but before you know it, you'll be right back where you were. For the moment, though, let's commit to taking things one day at a time."

Mom was really something. I knew that with all that had been going on with Ingrid, Opa, and me, life had to be almost too much for her to handle. But she remained positive, and her encouragement and counsel were just what I needed.

Drs. Peskin and Mowery made the rounds together on Sunday morning.

"I'm impressed by your diligence in exercising," Dr. Peskin noted. "The nurses tell me you're becoming a regular in walking laps around the halls out there."

"I want to get out of this place, if for no other reason than to regain my sanity. I mean, I've been here . . . how many days?"

"Almost a month," Dr. Mowery answered.

Dr. Peskin had a question. "How'd you like to get out of intensive care and back to the sixth floor?"

"You're kidding! Back to a regular room? I'd love it. Do you think I'm ready?" I almost couldn't believe what I was hearing.

Mom, Dad, and Ingrid arrived at lunch time as an entourage of nurses and orderlies readied me for the big move from the Trauma Unit to the sixth floor. One of the nurses was Helen Delgado.

"You're getting your old room back," she grinned. "And you're not the only one who feels great about that. We're all excited that you're back with us and one step closer to going home."

The whole family watched a pro football game on TV that afternoon, and then it was time for Ingrid to leave for the airport. She was finally returning to New York and her job with a publishing company.

Mom and Dad sensed that we wanted to be alone, so they quietly stepped into the hallway. Ingrid walked over to my bed and sat down next to me. "It looks like you're going to be all right," she started, not really knowing how to begin.

"I hope so." I squeezed her hands.

This was a tender moment for both of us. "It's hard to imagine after all you've been through, you're going to walk out of this place in a few days," she said.

"It sure didn't look like that a week ago, did it?"

"No, but you made it. I really think you're going to show them what can be done with a second chance."

At that moment, I felt a deep connection with Ingrid. Although she had been through a big ordeal herself, she was more concerned about me. We had always understood each other well and gotten along better than most siblings, but I sensed our relationship deepening. Now she was leaving, and I was going to miss her. I knew I was lucky to have such a special sister.

After Dad and Ingrid departed, Mom gave me some time to collect my feelings before taking me on another walk around the sixth-floor corridor. By this time, I had set my mind to walking six times daily, adding a lap each day. It was slow going at first, but as each day passed and each goal was set and accomplished, I felt my confidence build.

I must have looked like a man possessed as I doggedly pushed my IV pole with bags and bottles rattling through the hallways. Each time I shuffled past rooms and along the halls in slippers and hospital gown, I counted the laps. The exercise reminded me of the countless workouts I had put myself through in the past training camps . . . but this time the stakes were a lot higher.

OTHER SUPPORT

On Monday afternoon, Dad stopped by and took a walk with me around the corridor, making several laps before leading me back to my room. When he left, he said something that would have a profound effect on my life.

"I'm going to attend a meeting of the Crohn's and Colitis Foundation of America tonight at Scripps Hospital. They're organizing a local chapter."

"No kidding?" I said with real interest. "A lot of the cards and letters I've received have mentioned that organization. It seems like they've done a lot of good for a lot of patients."

"Yes, they have. I've been talking to a woman named Suzanne Rosenthal, who's here from New York. She said that the publicity you've created is causing their phones to ring off the hook. Your illness has brought the whole subject out of the closet. The CCFA wants to help you with anything you need during your recovery. Suzanne is a passionate lady, and I think you will enjoy getting to know her. It turns out she suffers from the same illness and was one of the co-founders of the organization."

On Tuesday, the last of the abdominal drains was removed, and I was given permission to take my first shower in nearly four weeks.

As I was wheeled to the shower unit, Carla warned me that I might get a little light-headed if I stood too long under the hot water. "Make sure you hold onto the handrails," she cautioned.

I listened but was a little more apprehensive about getting my incision wet for the first time. She assured me the water would be good for my stitched-up abdomen and that I shouldn't worry. As I carefully slipped my hospital gown off and eased under the shower, I turned my back to the spout. The warm water felt so good as it rolled over my shoulders and down my back. I stood for a few minutes reveling in a simple pleasure that I hadn't enjoyed in over a month. Cautiously, I turned around and carefully let some of the water roll down my chest and onto my abdomen and my incision. The sensation felt a little strange at first. Satisfied that the water wasn't hurting the open wound, I closed my eyes and let the soothing stream hit my face and chest and run in waves down the front of my body.

The scabbed-over incision and the two appliances hanging from my body were not a pretty sight—but it didn't matter. I stood there for fifteen minutes and let the warmth of the water slowly penetrate every pore on my body. The experience was heavenly!

The joy I felt, however, disappeared as quickly as the water ran down the drain. Back in my room, Mom looked puzzled and alarmed. "What's the matter?" she asked, noticing the sudden change of expression on my face.

"I don't know . . . I just feel very down. All of a sudden, I don't know how I'm going to handle all of this." Standing in the shower with my appliances felt great at first, but then was like—well, a cold shower of reality.

"But things are going so good right now," she reminded me.

"Maybe it's the ostomy bags. Maybe it's the uncertainty about my future. Maybe it's because Kris hasn't called," referring to my on-again, off-again girlfriend. Although I was improving physically, I continued to brood on the dark side, and I became more and more troubled and depressed.

I became an All-Pro worrier. I worried when my temperature made a relatively insignificant jump from 99.2 to 100.1 following a walk. I worried when a nurse I didn't know drew blood for a lab test. I worried about what I ate. I worried that I wasn't improving fast enough. I worried so much that I stopped realizing I was very lucky just to be alive.

I came to understand later that my sudden shifts into depression and feeling sorry for myself were natural reactions to the heavy medications and the enormous emotional impact of the surgery. Nearly everyone who has undergone ostomy surgery goes through them. A kind of grieving has to occur before someone can move forward and accept his or her new situation.

At home Friday morning, Dad and Mom talked about me over breakfast.

"It's terrible to see how depressed he is," Dad remarked. "He seems to feel better every day, but he continues to anticipate the worst, even though his temperature rarely tops 100 degrees anymore."

"I know. Yesterday was the first time he had to be coaxed out of bed to exercise."

"The bags. It must be those darn bags."

"It's a lot of things, I think," Mom said. "He even grew annoyed when I read some of the cards and letters to him yesterday. He told me he didn't want to hear any more."

Back at the hospital, Dad sought out Dr. Peskin to discuss what might be going on with me.

Dr. Peskin was direct. "Kurt, I don't think I have to tell you that this kind of operation is major in scope and has many potential consequences. Ostomy surgery is especially difficult for young people because it can be extremely damaging to their self-image. We had a rough start with all of the things that went wrong, but once we got the infection under control, the healing has progressed beautifully. Despite that, he's been through a lot, and his depressed state of mind is not unexpected. I do have some good news, though, that should lift everyone's spirits. It looks like Rolf might be able to go home Monday if there aren't any more setbacks."

My father looked relieved. "That will help," he said. "What's peculiar to us, though, is that Rolf seems to be upbeat and friendly with casual visitors, but when Marion and I come around, he changes and dumps everything on us."

"Again, that's normal. It's because you and Marion are safe to talk to. You're his parents. Getting counseling for him might be a good idea. I know that he has resisted seeing Dr. Ward, the staff psychologist, but it may be time to revisit that option."

Dad pondered that recommendation as he returned to my room to relay the good news. I was thrilled to hear that I would be going home soon. Monday, November 5 couldn't get here fast enough.

For the first time in a long time, I felt like I had something good to look forward to.

ANOTHER LESSON

A daily calorie count showed that I had taken in 3,428 calories on Thursday, most of them from rich protein shakes bolstered with supplements. I weighed only 123 pounds and desperately needed to gain some weight back. My gaunt, emaciated frame accentuated my rib cage, knobby knees, and elbows and was hard for me to look at. Was I really a professional athlete playing in the NFL just a few short weeks ago?

Besides trying to increase my weight, I was also learning how to deal with my ostomy.

"I hate this," I said during another demonstration from Melba on how to change the appliance.

Practice was starting to make perfect, however, and when I gave my first good return demonstration, Melba said, "Excellent! Now you're getting the idea."

I was beginning to understand the digestive rhythms of my body and discovered that it was best to change my appliances before breakfast. Melba taught me how to cut a new face plate to the correct size for my stoma, position the appliance, and properly "window frame" it with paper tape. The process didn't seem quite so overwhelming anymore, but changing my bags certainly wasn't routine yet either.

Just as we were finishing up, Phil Tyne, the Chargers strength and conditioning coach, stopped by to check on me. I was surprised to see him. After all, I had pretty much assumed my NFL career was over, so I wouldn't be needing his services any more. The truth was, though, that Phil and I had developed a great friendship and he was simply coming by to see how I was doing.

"I talked with your doctor, and he said that as soon as the sutures have been removed and your soreness is gone, we can begin the rehab process," he said.

"Great, Phil," I said sarcastically. "Where do we start? The two-mile run? How about some wind sprints followed by some sit-ups? Look at this body. Are you kidding me? It looks like I've been in a concentration camp. It's not going to be easy to do *anything* again."

"Yeah, but when was it ever easy? As I recall, you never did have much of a chest anyway." I looked up to see a wry grin on Phil's friendly face.

I would've laughed, but it would have hurt to do so because of my cut-open stomach.

"Rolf, there's no doubt you've been through a lot, but since you are still under contract with the team, when you finally get home and are able to get around again, you'll have full access to the weight room. I'm going to commit to you right now that I will help you get your body back."

He never mentioned "returning to play in The League," but that was okay with me. We both knew that notion was ludicrous and not even worth talking about. I just wanted to get healthy again and see if I could somehow return to a normal life of some kind. Just hearing him make that commitment to work with me gave me hope, and hope I would learn is a *very* powerful force.

Turns out I would need Phil a lot in the coming months. He would be the key to my recovery . . . my physical and emotional recovery. Phil became the person I would owe everything to. Without his encouragement, the long hours in the weight room, the many tears we would shed together, as well as the many times he just wouldn't give up on me, I know I would never have made it back.

The special bond that would develop between us is one we will both take to the grave.

NEW SIGHTS AND SOUNDS

It was a glorious, unseasonably warm late fall day in San Diego when Mom walked into my room late that afternoon. Like Phil, she had a grin on her face. "I just talked to Dr. Peskin, and he said that if you feel up to it, I can take you outside for half an hour of sunshine. What do you think?"

"Are you kidding? Let's go!"

Mom quickly grabbed an extra blanket, and together with Carla, they arranged all of my IV bottles and hung them on a wheelchair. The next thing I knew, we were heading down the corridor . . . the same corridor I had already shuffled around hundreds of times. Only this time, I was making a jailbreak for the elevator and my first chance to breathe fresh air in over five weeks.

The halls seemed to be more busy than usual. As we passed the admitting desk, there were several new patients waiting to get checked in, but I hardly noticed because I could see the front door and the radiant sunshine outside. My eyes began to adjust to the brightness, and I closed them for a moment, imagining what it would be like to leave this place for good.

Outside, we found a grassy area already occupied by several other patients. Mom stopped pushing the wheelchair, and together we soaked up the warmth of the sun and delighted in the fresh air. I drank in the sights and sounds like a man who thought he might never smell or taste the outdoors again.

"This is nice, Mom, really nice."

"Isn't it? You know, it won't be long now."

When we finally returned to my room, things suddenly didn't seem quite so bleak. "Mom, I'm beginning to feel better now . . . like I'll be able to deal with everything, no matter what happens in the future. I'm finally feeling a little bit hopeful again."

The outdoor walk did wonders for my psyche and seemed to buoy the spirits of my parents as well.

On Sunday morning, Dad arrived at University Hospital at 9 o'clock. By that time, I had already gone for three walks around the corridors and was eagerly anticipating my departure the next day.

In the afternoon, we watched the Chargers earn a hard-fought 20-14 victory in Kansas City. Mike Wood, my replacement, kicked two field goals that proved to be the margin of difference. I slept seven hours that night, and I was up walking the halls with Helen at 6:45 a.m. the next morning.

"I'm so excited," I said to my nurse. "I can hardly believe I'm finally going home. You've been such a help. It'll be fun to come back and visit you and Colleen after I've regained my weight and I'm in shape again. You won't even recognize me!"

"Caring for you has been a real pleasure," Helen said.

I wasn't so sure. "Oh, c'mon. I've been a horrible patient. I know that and you know that. I wouldn't have wanted to take care of me for anything."

"You haven't been that bad. Really. Besides, it's been kind of fun having a celebrity to take care of . . . even though we weren't allowed to tell anybody. We have never seen so much mail, which made us all a little jealous," she winked with a smile.

MONDAY, NOVEMBER 5

Discharge day was an emotional one. I was leaving a hospital and the doctors and nurses who had saved my life—but a life that had been changed forever. I knew I was a different person. In a sense, when the doctors removed part of my colon, they had also removed the last of my youthful innocence. At the time, I felt they may have robbed me of my future as well, but for the moment, I could only focus on today and tomorrow and not allow myself to think about anything beyond that.

After Mom and Dad packed up the remaining letters and all my new ostomy supplies, we all said a tearful thank you and goodbye to the nurses on duty and then headed down the hall towards the elevator. I felt like I knew every square inch of linoleum on that corridor but wouldn't mind if I never saw that flooring again.

As Mom and I waited outside for Dad to get the car, I enjoyed the brief moment to catch my thoughts . . . feeling a little like a man who had just been released from prison.

When Dad pulled up to the curb, I carefully got out of the wheelchair and slowly shuffled over to the car. The wire sutures still protruding from my abdomen made getting into the passenger seat uncomfortable, but I reminded my parents that the pain wasn't anything close to what I'd become accustomed to feeling every day while in the hospital.

I said very little on the ride home, choosing instead to take in the familiar landmarks passing by. Life had been going on as usual outside the walls of the hospital, but it seemed like I had been gone for a long time.

Although I was thrilled to finally get back to the house, the thirty-minute trip and all of the excitement of the day exhausted me. I needed to lie down, so my parents led me straight up to my old bedroom and eased me into the bed. I had become used to a hospital bed that you could raise and lower with the push of a button. Now, however, getting in and out of my old bed was much more troublesome. Anticipating this, Dad had tied a rope to the foot of my bed that would allow me to pull myself up with my arms and get out of bed without assistance.

I wouldn't need the rope that day, however. I wasn't going to be getting up anytime soon. This was a time to rest. I was tired and happy to be back home, in a quiet room without the beeps and clicks of monitors, and where nurses weren't going to interrupt me every few hours.

That night, sleep would come easily.

12

HOME SWEET HOME

For the first time in a long while, I got some real sleep. All night long, there wasn't a single interruption from nurses, residents, interns . . . or anyone else. No alarms went off, and there were no cleaning crews coming into my room to empty the trash or mop the floors.

I probably would have slept until noon if Mom hadn't been told how important it was to monitor my temperature. She finally woke me up—very gently—at 8 a.m.

During the seven long weeks in the hospital, I had often dreamed of being home in my old room, of Mom and Dad coming in to check on me, but there were a lot of times when it seemed like I'd never get out of there. Now that it had happened—being back home—I couldn't have been more grateful. More good news was that my temperature was normal, and it remained that way even after Mom joined me for a walk around the house. As we passed my parents' bedroom, I paused for a moment. I knew they had a scale in their bathroom.

What the heck, I thought. *I might as well know where ground zero is.*

"Can I check my weight?"

"Sure," Mom replied.

With a little trepidation and Mom on my heels, I shuffled into their bathroom and stepped on the scale. I weighed one hundred and twenty-six pounds—up three pounds from the hospital but more than sixty pounds below what I was listed at in the Chargers media guide.

"My new playing weight," I said with a smirk. Mom and I had a good laugh together.

After a couple of days, Mom drove me to downtown La Jolla, ten minutes away. I stayed in the car while she did a few errands, but I was thrilled to see familiar stores and watch shoppers strolling down Girard Avenue. Then she surprised me by dropping by the La Jolla Cove, one of the prettiest beaches in Southern California, with a lovely walkway rimming the cliffs above the ocean.

Mom suggested we get out and take a walk to enjoy the amazing view. As we shuffled along the path hand in hand, I quickly became overwhelmed at the beauty I was staring at, at the feeling of the warm sun on my face, the smell of the salt air, and the sounds of sea gulls overhead. Everything around me was such a contrast to the beeps of diagnostic monitors and the fluorescent lights I had been living with for almost two months that tears rolled down my cheeks. Once again, I realized how lucky I was to be alive.

The outing didn't last long but exhausted me nonetheless. I quickly fell asleep after we returned to the house but was roused when Dad came home. He had done some shopping and had purchased a present for me: a pair of oversized white bib overalls that fit loosely around my midsection. The farmer-style pants would enable me to move around easier and not snag the thirteen sutures that still protruded from my abdomen by more than an inch.

I put on my overalls and stood in front of the full-length mirror hanging on my bathroom door. "A real fashion statement," I said, studying my spindly arms sticking out from under the shoulder straps. I had a long way to go to get anywhere.

News from the Old Country

Fittingly, it was a gray and wet Wednesday morning—ten days after my release from the hospital—when Mom received a sad telephone call from Omi in West Germany. Opa had died in his sleep, succumbing peacefully after his long illness. Mom took the news stoically on the phone, but after she hung up, she sobbed deeply.

I pushed aside my protein shake and took her hand. "Oh, Mom. You've been through so much this past month."

"I felt so terrible, so guilty, when I was there," she admitted as she dabbed at the tears running down her cheeks. "All the time I was in Germany, I kept thinking I should have been back here with you and Ingrid. But now that he's gone, I'm so thankful I was there and able to see him alive one last time."

We talked for a while about Opa and what Mom's life was like growing up. Our mother-and-son discussion was good medicine for her. Mom's stories fascinated me, but our conversation was cut short by the need to change my ileostomy bag. This time, however, we didn't have our ostomy nurse, Melba, to help out. We were on our own for the first time, and the prospect frightened me.

With Mom's help, we carefully arranged all the supplies on the bathroom counter in front of us. We began the procedure by cutting the face plates to their proper size. No sooner had we removed one of the worn-out appliances than the stoma started to ooze. Caught unprepared, all we could do was watch in horror as liquid brown waste began leaking onto my stomach and slide slowly onto my clothes. Of course, the foul smell wasn't pleasant for either of us.

Mom quickly grabbed a washcloth and wiped up the mess.

"We've got to clean the skin around the stoma before we apply the adhesive paste," Mom reminded me. She had been studying the instructions that were sent home with me. Sensing urgency to get things moving, Mom rinsed the washcloth in soapy water and gently wiped around my stoma in preparation for applying the paste on my skin. Just as she finished, however, the stoma oozed again. Frustrated and flustered, we both got upset. Then Mom dropped the paste tube on the floor, and we just couldn't hold it in any more.

"Not again!" Mom said in an exasperated voice.

"I can't believe what's happening," I chimed in.

We were living Murphy's Law: anything that could go wrong did go wrong. We made five attempts at cleaning around the stoma, prepping the skin, and applying the paste before we were finally able to properly position the stupid bag. A procedure that should have taken not much longer than it takes to shave took us forty-five long, agonizing minutes.

"This is ridiculous," I declared in anger. "Is the rest of my life going to be like this?"

"Well, you better get used to it," Mom snapped back. She was every bit as upset as I was, and we had lost patience with each other. Neither of us was handling the situation well.

I was twenty-four years old, used to being self-reliant and in charge of my own life. But after two major operations, losing sixty pounds, and one huge incision, I could barely get out of bed on my own and was relying on my mother to go to the bathroom. Life was frustrating and humiliating, and I hated it.

As bad as the experience was, more concerning were the dark thoughts that followed.

What's it going to be like when Mom isn't around to help? And what about all this talk about resuming a normal life? That's a crock. This isn't going to be as easy as all those WOC nurses made it out to be. Is this the way it's going to be every time I have to change my bags?

I was really upset when the phone rang. By coincidence, a stoma nurse was on the line.

"Yes," Mom said, "we could use some help. Good, I'm glad to hear that you can drop by tomorrow. We'll look forward to seeing you, and yes, we do have some questions."

ALONE TIME

Dinner that evening was at 6 o'clock sharp, as it always was in my parents' house. Depending on the night of the week, the menu was often the same: spaghetti and meatballs one night, some kind of chicken dish another evening, cold cuts to mix things up, or a simple soup and a salad. For a special treat every now and then, Mom would cook *Wiener Schnitzel*, which I loved growing up.

On this evening, I joined them at the table, sitting in my customary seat at one end. Dad, as always, sat at the head, with Mom between us. I was still discouraged by the events earlier that day, so I wasn't feeling much like talking. Instead I sat sipping on a protein shake mixed with an egg and banana while they ate spaghetti and meatballs . . . my mind a million miles away.

"Are you sure you don't want some of this?" Mom asked, interrupting my thoughts.

"Okay, maybe just one meatball."

The meatball tasted delicious, but I knew not to press my luck and eat more than one.

Dad turned to Mom with a question. "Have you decided for sure that you're not going back for the funeral?"

"Yes, I think so. My brother said he'd fly to Germany to take care of the arrangements. There shouldn't be much to do, and I was just there to say goodbye to him. Thank God I had decided to go, even though it was tough with Ingrid and Rolf in the hospital. It gives me some solace now and a little bit of closure."

On Thursday morning Robert Honsik, a longtime friend, stopped by the house to check up on me. We had known each other for years and played a lot of tennis together since our days at La Jolla High.

I was sitting on the patio, enjoying the sunshine and trying to read a book when Mom brought Robert through the house into the back yard.

"Hey, buddy," I said, slowly getting to my feet. We shook hands and embraced awkwardly.

We hadn't seen each other since I'd gone into the hospital, but it was obvious that Robert was shocked at my appearance. Although he tried his best to hide his reaction, he wasn't prepared for what he saw.

"You look like you've gone through hell," he remarked, shaking his head.

"Then looks don't lie. I feel like I have," I answered with a rue smile.

Robert couldn't stop staring. "I knew you were going to be skinny, but this is ridiculous!"

"I know. Kinda crazy, huh? But I'm starting to get better. I know you could run me all over the tennis court *now*, but don't get used to it because it's not going to last. I'm going to be back . . . promise you."

I could tell Robert didn't believe me. I knew he was wondering if I'd *ever* be able to play tennis again, much less beat him again.

Still, I found myself marveling at our conversation. Two weeks ago, I was fighting for my life, unsure if I would live. A fortnight later, I was talking to a good friend about running each other around on a tennis court. Life was changing in a hurry, and I couldn't wait.

"I tried to visit you in the hospital," Robert began, "but they wouldn't let me in. I talked to your parents a few times, but I didn't really want to bother them, so I listened to the radio and read the newspaper, just like everyone else. Wow, you've had a rough time, but I'm so glad you made it."

"Don't feel bad about it. You tried. I know you would have come if you could have. The fact is they wouldn't let *anyone* visit. I'll never forget all the cards and flowers though, and all the prayers said for me. That support really made a difference."

Before we could continue the conversation, Mom came out to the back yard. "Someone else is here to see you," she said.

I looked up and saw Dr. Peskin step onto the patio. He smiled in approval of what he saw.

"Home cooking is obviously doing you some good, Rolf. You look like you're beginning to put on some weight."

I glanced at Robert, who no doubt could hardly believe what he had just heard.

"Dr. Peskin, this is an old high school buddy, Robert Honsik. He wants to know when he'll be able to start whipping me in tennis again."

Dr. Peskin laughed. "Well, that won't be for a while," he said, "but I have a hunch we'll all be amazed at how quickly you'll come around. And now, Robert, if you'll excuse us for a couple of minutes, I need to examine Rolf."

"No, Doctor," I jumped in. "If you don't mind, I'd like Robert to see this. He's a great friend, and I'm going to have to lean on him during the next few months. I'd prefer that he know exactly what's going on, if he doesn't mind."

Robert nodded yes, a little unsure of what he was about to see.

"Okay, then let's take a look." Dr. Peskin opened the front of my oversized bathrobe, revealing my hideous midsection: thirteen wire sutures holding together a black, crusted-over surgical incision that looked like it might never close.

The sight was almost more than Robert could stand. He inhaled sharply and his face flushed in shock, but he gathered himself quickly. Dr. Peskin proceeded with his examination.

"Looks like you're coming along just fine. Everything is healing beautifully, and in ten days or so we should be able to start taking the sutures out."

"You really think so?" I asked hopefully. The wires were a painful nuisance and kept getting snagged on my clothes. I would be thrilled to have them gone.

"I sure do. You've gone five days now with normal-range temperatures. Your blood pressure has stabilized, and your mother tells me you weighed in at 128 pounds this morning, up five pounds since you left the hospital. Things are certainly looking up," my surgeon said optimistically.

I believed him, but Robert must have thought we were both crazy. He stood in the background, trying to recover from what he had just witnessed.

Neither of us knew at the time, however, how important he would be to my recovery.

13

ONE MAILBOX AT A TIME

FRIDAY, NOVEMBER 9

The next afternoon, I had another visitor—Gordon Jennings, who lived next door to my condo. Although I had not been back to my own place for almost two months, he had heard on the radio that I was recuperating with my parents, so he decided to stop by to say hello.

It was a beautiful afternoon, and Gordon must have sensed my desire to get out of the house. "We could drive up the coast," he offered after a short time catching up. "We can go anywhere you want. You must be going nuts after being cooped up for so long."

"Hey, that'd be neat. You can't believe how many times I've dreamed about seeing the beach again."

With Gordon's help, I gingerly climbed into the passenger side of his two-seater sports car, and we headed north on Pacific Coast Highway past the Torrey Pines bluffs and through the beach communities of Del Mar, Solana Beach, and Encinitas. The scenery was breathtaking! The low November sun shone brilliantly, and we rolled down the windows to take in the whole experience.

"Gordon, this is unbelievable! It's just like I imagined it would be. As long as I live, I'll never take life and these simple pleasures for granted again."

Gordon and I were gone for almost two hours. When we returned to the house, I thanked him for his kindness as he helped me out of his car. What a day . . . it was just what I needed.

As Gordon drove away, however, I became concerned that our

excursion might have caused me to develop a temperature. But it was satisfying to see the thermometer stop at 99.2, the highest it had been since my discharge, but still comfortably within normal range.

"Hallelujah!" Mom exclaimed. "That's wonderful." She was always taking my temperature and cheered each time it was normal.

The good feelings didn't last very long, however. That night, while sitting at the dinner table with my parents, my abdomen throbbed painfully around the wire sutures. I tried to keep it to myself, but . . . .

"Rolf, what's wrong? What is it?" Mom asked, noticing me wincing.

"Nothing, really."

"C'mon," Dad chimed in. "Your face is a dead giveaway. What's hurting?"

"Well, actually my sutures are really bothering me. It feels as though each one is like a tiny knife pricking me every time I move."

Dad knew exactly what was happening.

"Well, your skin *is* getting cut," he explained. "As you gain weight and your stomach stretches, the wire sutures can't expand. They're actually cutting into your skin. It's nothing serious, but you're going to have to bite the bullet until they come out."

I slept sporadically that night. The ache of the wires persisted, so in the morning I put a call into Dr. Peskin to let him know what was going on.

"Nothing to be alarmed about," he responded, helping to allay my concerns. "As long as you don't spike any more fevers and you feel good, you should be fine until we take the wires out."

"That's good to hear. After all the things that happened to me in the hospital, I was just worried that something else might be going wrong," I explained a little apologetically.

"I can understand that," Dr. Peskin said in a reassuring voice. "The worst is over for you. You're well on the road to recovery. I'll bring some pain pills over later today to help take the edge off. Use them if you need to, and we'll take another look at the sutures then."

Dad came home for lunch just as Mom and I were coming back from my morning walk.

"Weigh-in time," he announced. I stepped up on the bathroom scale and watched the dial spin to 129, up a pound from two days earlier. Another sign things were heading in the right direction.

Surrounded by bathroom mirrors, I was fascinated by my gaunt frame. I raised my right arm and tried to flex my bicep. Not much happened. The sight made me laugh, and Dad joined in.

Then he had an idea. He walked over to the hall closet and pulled out his trusty 35mm camera. "I want to take some pictures of you so that when you're healthy, you'll remember how sick you were. You know, some before-and-after shots."

As Dad began taking pictures of me in my shorts, I remarked, "Look at this body. Have you ever seen anything quite so pathetic?"

"Not much muscle, that's for sure."

"And this scar. Did you ever see anything so ugly?"

He responded by taking a close-up of the incision that split my abdomen in two, still being held together by the thirteen grotesque wire sutures and flanked on either side by an ostomy bag. It was not a pretty sight.

The next morning, Sunday, November 11, I had put on another pound and weighed 130 pounds, up nearly five pounds in the six days since my discharge from the hospital. Since my old appetite had returned, Mom prepared my favorite meal—*Wiener Schnitzel*—while Dad and I sat down to watch the Chargers play the Cincinnati Bengals. In a game the Chargers were supposed to win, San Diego had to rally late to defeat the Bengals, 26-24. The Chargers scored ten points in the fourth quarter, including a game-winning field goal by my replacement, Mike Wood, his fourth of the day.

"Remarkable!" I said to Dad. "The team is 8-3, and if they can beat the powerful Steelers next Sunday, there's no telling how far they can go."

I was excited for my old team, but I also felt a deep sense of regret and sadness that I was no longer a part of what was going on.

BACK IN TRAINING

The next day, I put myself on a walking program that I measured by the mailboxes on our street. In training, every athlete needs a goal. Mine was adding at least one mailbox to my walk each day. That doesn't sound like a lot, particularly in California, where the houses are unusually close to each other, but I needed to start somewhere. My goal was to get strong enough to walk up and down Prestwick Drive without stopping.

I began with two mailboxes. On Tuesday, I added two more. By Wednesday, I was up to eight, and I actually had a little spring in my step. Friends and neighbors, driving by in their cars, slowed down to wave encouragement as they watched me shuffle along in my baggy sweatsuit. Those walks were great times to reflect on what I had been through. I was still unsure of the future, still needing to take things one day at a time, but I was beginning to feel alive again.

On Thursday morning, after a wonderful walk in the sun, I sat down at the breakfast table and downed a glass of orange juice.

I looked up at Mom. "I really think I'm going to be able to handle this," I said out of the blue. "It's going to be okay. Somehow things are going to work out, even if I don't know exactly how."

She sat down next to me and smiled. "I know you're going to be fine. It won't be easy, but you're going to make it. We just have to remember that it takes little steps—"

"—to climb a mountain," I interrupted. "And, boy, are you right about that."

That night I got a surprise visit from Doc Brooks, our popular equipment manager.

"Hey, man, how ya doin'?" he said in that jovial voice of his. "The fellas have been wondering about you."

"Doc, it's so great to see you. It's really nice of you to come by. You won't believe it, but a couple of weeks ago I couldn't make it across this living room. Now I'm starting to take short walks by myself. I'm still not ready for much more than that, but it's a start."

"That's great. Me and a bunch of the guys were talking, and we were wondering if you were feeling well enough to come out to the stadium this Sunday for the Steelers game."

I hesitated. "Well, I don't know. I haven't thought about doing anything like that. I haven't left the house for anything other than a couple of short drives. Where would I sit?"

"Don't worry, Rolf. You and your parents just be at the Player's Gate an hour or so before game time. Tickets will be waiting for you. If you get a chance, try to come down to the locker room before the game to see the fellas."

I knew I had to get approval from Dr. Peskin before considering an outing to the stadium. But it did sound exciting. On Saturday, he stopped by to begin removing the thirteen wire sutures. He came armed with wire cutters and a pair of pliers that he could have bought at a local hardware store. I looked at the barbaric tools and wondered how this was going to work.

"I'm not going to kid you," the surgeon began. "This is going to hurt like hell for a minute or two. That's why I'm going to do it in stages over the next week—three or four sutures at a time every couple of days."

Dr. Peskin walked back into the house and called for my mother. "Marion, we need your help for a moment. This is going to be painful for Rolf, and I need someone to distract him."

When a doctor says, "This is going to hurt" . . . then it's going to *really* hurt.

Wanting to get this procedure over with as soon as possible, I took off my shirt and positioned myself on the patio lawn chair, gripping the armrests as tightly as possible. "Okay," I said, bracing myself. "Let's get going."

"What I'm about to do is simple," Dr. Peskin said. "I'm going to snip one end of the wire suture—that part won't hurt. But then I'm going to have to twist and pull the wire out . . . and that will be painful. Are you ready?"

I nodded and steeled myself for what was to come.

With Mom talking to distract me, I tried not to watch. When Dr. Peskin snipped the first wire, it sounded like a wire wrapped around a bundle of newspapers being cut. Dr. Peskin was right; that didn't hurt. The pain started when he began to pull the wire out.

He held my shoulder as he tugged and twisted the wire, and I clenched my teeth and grunted. He hadn't lied . . . this *was* painful.

"Hold on, we're almost there," Dr. Peskin said. "Just a little bit more

. . . and that's it." He straightened up, took a deep breath, and held a three-inch piece of wire triumphantly in the air. I relaxed my grip on the arms of the lawn chair as beads of sweat formed on my forehead.

"One down," the doctor announced.

Then I remembered he wanted to do two more sutures.

"Okay. Let's keep going and get this over with," I said.

Dr. Peskin grasped hold of the next wire with his pliers, snipped it, and then began pulling. The pain was bad, but truthfully, it lasted only a moment. Well, maybe longer than a moment, but before I knew it, he had all three sutures out. When he had finished, Mom went inside and returned with refreshments and a towel for my sweaty face. It was time for a little celebration.

"Three more visits to get the last ten out," Dr. Peskin announced. "Monday and Tuesday . . . and maybe Thursday, Thanksgiving Day, for the last session. Would that be okay?"

"Fine with me," I replied. "The sooner the better. But Doc, before you go I have to ask you something. I've been invited by the team to watch the Chargers game tomorrow at the stadium. Do you think it would be possible for me to go?"

Dr. Peskin looked at me as he carefully considered his answer. He saw the anticipation in my eyes and heard the excitement in my voice.

"Rolf, if you feel up to it, you should go. Just remember you're still very weak, and this outing will be quite strenuous. If you have some place to sit and relax and someone there to assist you, I think the fresh air and change of scenery might be really good for you."

"Thanks, Doc. It'll be great to see the guys again."

CHEERS AND TEARS

I walked into the kitchen as Dad was marking another day off on the wall calendar. I didn't know it then, but the new date—Sunday, November 18, 1979—would be a day I'd remember forever.

I was about to go watch the Chargers play the defending Super Bowl champion Pittsburgh Steelers in a crucial football game for both teams. Even though I wasn't playing, I found myself getting nervous, almost as if I were suiting up. It was hard to believe that it had been only eight weeks since I had last set foot in an NFL stadium. Had it really been only two months since I had collapsed on the team plane coming back from New England?

But I didn't have much time to dwell on those thoughts. Right now, I needed to get ready for the game. I didn't have a lot of choices in wardrobe . . . it was my new "uniform"—the big white painter overalls and a sweatshirt—that would have to do.

My parents and I arrived at San Diego Stadium ninety minutes before kickoff and were escorted to seats in the private box of General Manager Johnny Sanders.

I sat there for a few minutes, soaking in the familiar sights and sounds of pregame warmups that are part of the ritual before every NFL game. Players jogged and stretched and got ready in their own unique way as coaches strolled the neatly lined stadium grass, preparing for the upcoming contest.

I was anxious to get down to the locker room before things got too hectic. Sensing this, Rick Smith, the Chargers public relations director, led me to the elevator. On the way, we passed several sportswriters—who did double takes. From their looks, I could tell that they almost didn't recognize me in my emaciated condition. I exchanged pleasantries, but I was looking forward to getting downstairs.

When we arrived at the locker room, the first guy I ran into was Doc Brooks. He was sporting an ear-to-ear grin as he stuck out his hand to shake mine. He quickly sized me up, and like a good equipment manager, said, "That uniform will never do."

"Doc, I don't need anything else. I just came down to say hello to the guys and wish everyone good luck."

Doc and Rick led me through the doorway into the players' private world. Suddenly, everything came back to me. The stereo was going full blast, and the guys were in various stages of dress getting ready for the game. On a couple of cushioned tables, teammates were getting stretched by the training staff while others were taking one last glance at their playbooks.

Phil Tyne, our strength coach, noticed me first. He literally dropped the leg of the defensive back he was stretching to come over and greet me. "Wow, Rolf, what a surprise!" he said. "It's great to see you. You look a helluva lot better than when I last saw you in the hospital."

A gruff voice called out from behind me. "Hey, Benirschke! Where'd you get those designer overalls?" It was our leader, quarterback Dan Fouts, irreverent as usual.

Before I could respond, Louie Kelcher, our massive but gentle All-Pro defensive tackle, came up and carefully wrapped his six-foot-five-inch frame around me.

"Easy," I grinned. Then I remembered the time he came to visit me in the intensive care unit but was told that visits were strictly limited to immediate family.

"But I'm a family member," he had told the nurse indignantly. "I'm his big brother, Louie Benirschke."

Since Louie weighed well north of the pounds he was listed at, was a good half-foot taller than me, spoke with a Texas accent, and didn't look at all like me, the nurse had good reason to be skeptical. Maybe it was his charm or maybe she was frightened by this mountain of a man . . . whatever it was . . . she had allowed this "big brother" to see me—a memory we both smile about today.

After catching up briefly with most of my teammates, Louie, unbeknownst to me, stepped away and sought out Coach Don Coryell.

"What do you think if we make Rolf honorary captain for the day?" Louie asked. He, along with tackle Russ Washington, were co-captains, although Louie was still recovering from a knee injury sustained in training camp and wouldn't be playing.

Coach Coryell didn't bat an eye. "Heck, yes," he said with his well-chronicled lisp. "We sure should. I think it's a great idea, and the guys will love it."

Louie came back a few moments later and told me what he had just done. "I just spoke with Coach, and you, good buddy, are going to be one of the captains for today's game. That means you'll have to come out on the field with me and Russ for the coin toss before the opening kickoff."

I tried to object, but Louie would have none of that. I honestly didn't know if I'd have the strength to walk that far. But Louie didn't care. "Don't worry about it, little man. If you can't walk all the way, I'll just carry you!"

Before I could protest any more, Doc Brooks emerged from his office with my number 6 game jersey and helped me put it on over my overalls. I reminded Louie and Russ that I'd have to walk slowly—very slowly—because of the wire sutures still cutting into my tender abdomen.

While I was collecting my thoughts, the rest of the players were returning to the locker room from pre-game warm-ups. We were about ten minutes from kickoff, and I could feel the tension mounting as I sat quietly in a corner, wondering how this was all going to play out.

With about four minutes before we were to take the field, Coach Coryell, a master motivator, began with one of his special pre-game pep talks. I always felt that Coryell didn't miss very much, and he proved it that afternoon. "Listen up, everybody," he said. "We have a special visitor today. Rolf came down to check up on us. I'm happy to tell you he's going to be one of our co-captains today."

The players exploded in cheers and applause. I must have been quite a sight, sitting there next to all those giant men with my skinny frame draped by my oversized Chargers jersey. I was genuinely touched by their thoughtfulness but just wanted to get out of the way. I didn't feel like I belonged. My teammates were about to do battle with one of the NFL's marquee teams, and they didn't need any distractions.

I watched the players file out of the locker room and waited until everyone had left before I followed. Just before leaving, I paused and looked back at the messy dressing room. I sadly wondered if this would be the last time I'd experience a locker room on game day.

As I slowly shuffled down the tunnel and onto the field, I headed toward the Chargers bench just as the offense was being introduced to the year's largest home crowd. I looked up into the stands and wondered what my parents were thinking. I had been gone for more than forty-five minutes.

When the Marine Corps band played the National Anthem, I lined up with the rest of the players on the sidelines. What an awesome feeling! Most athletes experience overpowering feelings of pride, excitement, and a little nervousness as they stand listening to the *Star-Spangled Banner*. Those same feelings rippled through me with even greater intensity at that moment. A ton of emotions were flowing through my head.

When the National Anthem was finished, I turned to find Louie. I was worried I would take too long to walk to midfield and was comforted when he put his arm around my shoulders. Just then the voice of the public address announcer snapped me back to reality. "And now, ladies and gentlemen, the team captains for today's game . . . ."

After introducing the Pittsburgh captains, my heart began pounding. The crowd watched expectantly as Louie, Russ, and I began walking slowly to midfield. I could sense a low buzzing from the crowd, but it changed dramatically when the PA announcer blared, "Ladies and gentlemen, San Diego Chargers captains Russ Washington, Louie Kelcher, and, returning for the first time in many weeks, Rolf Benirschke!"

As if in unison, the 52,000-plus fans rose to their feet and began applauding and cheering. The noise grew louder and louder and caught me completely by surprise. By the time we reached midfield, I could feel tears starting to form. I was overwhelmed by this spontaneous demonstration of encouragement and just couldn't keep it together.

At that moment I was pretty sure this was the last time I would ever walk onto a football field, but it didn't matter . . . I was just happy to be alive and so grateful. The emotions that I had tried to hold in check over the past two months came gushing out. Like a dam that had broken, tears flowed freely down my cheeks.

Well, at least Mom and Dad know where I am, I thought. When we reached midfield, the Pittsburgh co-captains greeted me with warm smiles and handshakes. "Mean Joe" Greene, one of the greatest Steelers of all-time, yelled above the din of the crowd, "These people must really care for you." Then Jack Lambert, another hard-nosed Pittsburgh standout, shouted, "Hey, Rolf! Welcome back."

The officials, caught up in the emotion, allowed the cheering to go on for several minutes before making the coin flip. "Mean Joe" made the call, but I couldn't hear a thing. The moment was magic for me.

Apparently, it was a memorable occasion for others as well. A few years later, Chargers owner Gene Klein described this scene in his autobiography, *First Down and a Billion*:

> In the two decades I owned the team, that was the most heart-wrenching moment I experienced. We all knew Rolf's football career was over. We just wondered if this was the last time we were going to see him alive!

We won the coin toss, and Louie escorted me back to the bench, holding my left hand in his giant paw—just in case. All the time, the huge crowd never stopped cheering and applauding. I waved to say thank you and felt like I was walking on air.

By the time the game started, I was exhausted and completely wiped out, emotionally and physically. I knew I had to get back to the security of the box and sit down. Always thinking ahead, Rick Smith was right there to help me off the field and escort me back upstairs.

We happened to leave in the middle of a play, but as the fans near the exit tunnel saw us approaching, they stood up again and cheered once more. The rest of the Chargers fans throughout the stadium picked up on what was happening, and they followed suit. An impromptu stadium wave developed, and, for the second time in ten minutes, I was completely overcome with emotion.

I can honestly say those few minutes were the most thrilling of my life. The crowd's response had taken me totally by surprise, but what I didn't realize was that moment would play a very important part in my eventual recovery.

The heavily favored Steelers may have been the defending Super Bowl champions—and on their way to another NFL crown—but that day my inspired teammates went out and destroyed Pittsburgh, 35-7. Fans who were there that Sunday still talk about that game.

That night, I enjoyed my best sleep in two years.

14

It Takes Little Steps

One of my problems—and it was a nice one to have—was how to put weight back on. Since my release from the hospital, I had gained seven or eight pounds, but that came with a price. The more weight I added, the more the wire sutures would cut deeper into my skin—and it hurt!

So today—Thanksgiving Day—was a problem. I knew I would be stretching my stomach even more than usual and, hopefully, put on a few more pounds after eating a big holiday meal. I could smell the turkey Mom was cooking, and I couldn't wait to dig in. I also couldn't wait for the final wires to come out of my stomach, even though I knew the last set would be even more painful than the first batch.

Late Thanksgiving morning Dr. Peskin stopped by, as promised, to complete the task. These sutures would be the most difficult because they were deeply embedded in the muscle next to my belly button. Just getting to them would be a problem. Dr. Peskin recognized the challenge and thought it would be a good idea to inject the area with novocaine before he went to work. I agreed with him wholeheartedly, but even then, the experience turned out to be a miserable ordeal that left me shaking and sweating. I was really relieved when the last tug and pull was over.

Once the final wire suture was yanked out, it was like my appetite was allowed to run wild. All I could think about was eating a plateful of gravy-covered turkey and stuffing, and that's what I did—twice. I ate more food that day than I had in several years!

Sitting uncomfortably full on the couch afterward, I couldn't help but thank my parents again for all they had done for me and for the greatest gift the Lord had given me . . . the gift of life.

A week later, Robert Honsik dropped by for another visit. After chitchatting for a while, my longtime friend asked me what I was thinking for myself down the road. Until then, I really hadn't given my long-term future much thought. I had been so focused on getting through each day that I had purposefully avoided thoughts of the future. While being in that mode had helped me survive my difficult hospital stay and the early weeks back at home, Robert's question reminded me that it was time to begin facing the future.

"I'm not sure," I reflected.

"Do you think you'll ever kick again?" my friend probed.

"Are you kidding me? Look at me!" The thought of ever playing pro football again with an ostomy seemed so ludicrous that it wasn't even worth talking about. No one had ever come back from ostomy surgery before, and everyone knows how ruthless the NFL can be. There are hundreds of guys waiting in line for every position, desperate for a chance to play.

Then the memory of walking into the Chargers locker room just before the Pittsburgh game returned to me. That was a rush, and I loved everything about it: the blaring music, the tension of the upcoming game, the camaraderie of the players, and the idea of competing at the highest level before a stadium full of fans and a national TV audience. It was heady stuff even though there were times when the whole experience could be frightening . . . like walking a high-wire without a net.

The more I reflected, the more I believed these thoughts: *I will never be able to do that again. Football is over. Get used to it and move on.*

Yes, but to what? I wondered.

For the next few days, as I walked past mailboxes on Prestwick Drive, I spent a lot of time contemplating my future. I had gotten my degree in Zoology and always wondered if I should return to some kind of wildlife biology or work with endangered species . . . perhaps at the San Diego Zoo. But football had opened up a whole new world to me—the world of sports, entertainment, and business. I had become connected in the San Diego community and loved learning about new kinds of companies and how the owners had gotten them started.

The more I wondered about what lay ahead, though, the more confused, frustrated, and depressed I became. I just didn't know what I should do or would be good at doing or even what I *could* do now that I had to wear ostomy bags. Then I remembered a couple of WOC nurses telling me: *Your ostomy bags shouldn't keep you from doing anything you want.* If I could only believe them . . . but I just wasn't sure that I could at this stage. I became really discouraged and more unsure than ever about my future.

IMPORTANT ENCOURAGEMENT

For weeks, I had been receiving mail that had been forwarded to me from the Chargers, and many of the notes resonated with me. They were the most encouraging and heartfelt letters from people living with ostomies, and they seemed to explode the restrictive lifestyle box I presumed I would have to live within now that I was wearing a bag.

In fact, as the letters poured in, I was not only amazed at the courage and perseverance so many demonstrated in returning to whatever it was that they loved to do, but the things they actually *did*. There just didn't seem to be any limitations. Here is one such letter:

> Rolf, I am writing to you about my wife, Darlene. It all started nearly four years ago shortly after the birth of our second daughter, Kristen. It seemed like everything Darlene ate or drank gave her such pain and terrible bowel movements that life was almost unbearable for her. We couldn't go out to dinner, see a show, or go dancing without knowing first exactly where the ladies' rooms were located.
>
> We went to a specialist, but after all kinds of tests, he sent my wife to a psychiatrist to make sure the pain she was experiencing was not in her head. We knew it

was not. The pain grew worse, and Darlene practically stopped eating because of the aggravation it caused.

It was at that point that she was finally diagnosed as having a form of colitis. She was put on Prednisone, and doctors limited her work and outside activities. She got better for a while, but within a year, Darlene needed two surgeries to remove most of her large colon and part of her small intestine. But her condition did not improve, so more surgery was required.

Darlene has now had a total of thirteen operations. She could have given up very easily, but she insisted that she would beat this disease before it beat her.

Between everything, Darlene has still found time to raise our two daughters, run a household, and hold down a steady job. Oh yes, she also bowls in three leagues, goes camping, and is a wonderful wife, friend, and lover to her husband.

I've read that you've had two surgeries, and that you've gone through a lot. You may have thought at one time that you would be better off dead than wear a bag. Don't think that!

Darlene's only real wish is that a cure for colitis is found and found soon so that other people, young or old, do not have to go through what she has gone through.

We both want to wish you all the best.

After pondering this inspiring letter and many others like it, I finally screwed up enough courage to ask Dr. Peskin if he thought there was a chance I might be able to play sports again. I was thinking about tennis and swimming and skiing . . . kicking a football wasn't even a thought.

His answer caught me completely by surprise. "Absolutely! You'll be able to play all of the sports you played prior to your operation. You can even kick again if you want, Rolf. Nothing that's happened—the illness, the surgery, the ostomy, having to wear appliances—need stop you from playing again. I'm not aware of anyone kicking or playing football at any level with an ostomy, but that doesn't mean it can't be done."

As we neared Christmas, I made an early New Year's resolution: I would get into the best shape possible and see what happens.

GETTING IN SHAPE

For more than a year, I had lost all desire for food. When I first became ill, it didn't take long to figure out that eating food started a chain reaction of bad things. The first effect was often nausea. This was followed by severe intestinal pain and bad abdominal cramping. Lastly, and the most difficult thing to deal with, was the uncontrollable diarrhea and the need to *always* know where a bathroom was.

For some people with IBD, eating is no longer an option—the only way they can receive their nutrition is intravenously. Fortunately, I had to experience total parenteral nutrition (TPN) or "hyperalimentation" only for a little while. I have now met many people, however, who get their nutrition exclusively by hooking themselves up to an IV line inserted into their neck or chest at night, where they remain connected for hours to receive the necessary nutrients and calories to sustain them.

Imagine never experiencing the pleasure of eating real food of any kind . . . no chicken fajitas, no lasagna, no strawberries, and no Häagen Dazs! People do and carry on living normal lives, demonstrating once again that the human spirit can cope with almost anything when the alternative is not being alive.

As 1979 came to a close, food became a pleasure once again, and I was thrilled. I couldn't get enough of all the good-tasting things I had missed, and the results were showing up on the bathroom scale almost daily. You can't imagine how encouraging it was for me to see my weight climb to 132 . . . 133 . . . 134. I still had a long way to go, but I was taking small steps and making progress. I knew that those were the kind of steps I needed to get to the top of the mountain.

I learned by trial and error that I had to be cautious about what I ate. My gut did much better when I avoided certain stringy vegetables, nuts, and fruits with skins. Too much popcorn was a problem, and I learned that certain foods caused more gas than others. Nevertheless, I discovered that I really had few limitations and nothing could take away the joy of eating again.

In early December, Phil Tyne, our strength coach, surprised me by giving me a set of one- and two-pound dumbbells.

"Here, work with these while you're reading or watching television. We won't miss them in the Chargers weight room," he teased.

I looked at my skinny arms and recognized again I had a long way to go. The weights Phil had given me were for young kids or senior citizens, but for me, those light dumbbells were all I could lift. But at least I was alive, and that was a starting point.

Although Phil was just doing for me what he would do for any other player, his dedication was instrumental to my comeback. I would come to rely on him for encouragement and inspiration over the hard months of conditioning that lay ahead.

"Don't push yourself too hard," Phil cautioned the next time I saw him. "We can't afford to rush things and get you injured when you're just starting out."

I had just moved out of my parents' house and back to my condominium, but I was becoming bored with taking walks on my own. Phil sensed that, so he suggested I start coming down to the Chargers practices at the stadium. I was delighted. The team was in a playoff drive, and there was real excitement in the air.

Invigorated by the atmosphere, I wanted to get at it. Phil knew I had to take things slowly. The first day we met, we started by taking a leisurely jog down the length of the football field. Then we walked the width of the field and jogged back down the other sideline. The light exercise was strange and scary and exciting and tiring all at once. I was a little overwhelmed at how far I had to go, but Phil wouldn't let me dwell on that.

After our short run, Phil brought me into the Chargers weight room and announced, "The place to begin is at the core of your body—the abdominal muscles."

Of course, my core had been sliced open—twice—so the thought of trying to do a sit-up was painful and frightening. Doctors say it takes about six weeks for muscles to fully knit together after an operation. That much time had elapsed, so I was now "safe" to begin exercising my stomach muscles, even if I was a little tentative. Phil knew I couldn't do a full sit-up so we began by doing a few "lean-ups," where I would stand next to the wall with my feet about one foot from the wall and my shoulders leaning against it . . . and then try to stand up straight. It sounds ridiculously easy as I write this, but it was hard for me to do at the time.

We then proceeded to the weight machines, where it didn't take long before I was whipped. My scrawny muscles—whatever I had left of them—quivered as I walked out of the weight room that first day.

The Chargers had a great year, finishing with a 12-4 record, matched in the AFC only by the defending Super Bowl champion Steelers. But since we had crushed Pittsburgh on that memorable afternoon when I had served as honorary captain, the Chargers would have home-field advantage right up to Super Bowl XIV, if necessary.

Unfortunately, the Chargers season came to an abrupt and disappointing end, losing to the wild-card Houston Oilers in the first round of the playoffs. Houston had come into San Diego decimated by injuries and decided underdogs, but they shocked everyone with a stunning 17-14 upset win.

As I watched my teammates jog off the field, heads down and upset, I hurt for them and wondered what the future held for all of us.

15

LARGER THAN ME

Following the devastating loss to the Houston Oilers, the Chargers organization knew they had all the pieces in place—except maybe a kicker—to make another run and get back to the playoffs. As for me, my future was completely up in the air, and the thought of kicking again was something I still couldn't even consider. All of my focus was on getting healthy again.

In late January, I stepped up my workouts. Phil Tyne urged me not to go too hard until I had gained a little more weight. "You just don't have much stamina yet," he cautioned.

I discovered he was absolutely right when I tried to play tennis with my buddy Robert Honsik for the first time. I was amazed at how weak I felt and how slowly I moved around the court; it felt like I was running in combat boots. The good news was that I was playing again and able to hit the ball without pain. The best news, though, was that my ostomy bags stayed on and didn't get in the way during thirty minutes of running around the court.

I was getting used to the feeling of wearing the appliances and getting more confident every day. As I continued to gain weight and get stronger, I was amazed at how quickly my body was recovering.

My mind was a different story. I was so unsure of what the future held that I found myself wondering . . . wondering what I was going to do with my life, wondering if I could go back into the ocean and body surf, wondering what traveling would be like, and wondering if

I would ever date again . . . or marry. I tried to stay in the present and control what I could control, but it was a challenge.

I continued to eat well and put on weight while I read inspirational books to occupy my mind. By late March, I weighed just over 150 pounds—hardly anything to write home about when it comes to pro football, but I knew I was healing and getting stronger. There were periods of self-doubt, but I fought hard to counteract them by counting my blessings. I was alive and had my health back, and I had great friends and a family who had demonstrated that they would do anything for me.

Then out of nowhere, I was offered a job as a radio and TV commentator for the San Diego Sockers, a professional soccer team in the now-defunct North American Soccer League. Since I loved the game and had played soccer in high school and college, this was a natural fit, but I was also intrigued by the opportunity. More than that, I wondered if this might be a profession I could get into. I thought it would be interesting to see if I was good at broadcasting and if I enjoyed covering sports from the media side.

I accepted the job and loved learning what it took to be a broadcaster and feeling comfortable in front of a camera and a live microphone. Since most of the games were in the evenings or on weekends, I could continue my daily workouts with Phil.

Being associated with the Sockers helped with my comeback. The Sockers often needed another player to round out teams in their "small-side" practice games and asked me to fill in. Soon I became a regular—although I was cautious at first—and loved trying to hold my own against world-class soccer players. The focus was on conditioning, with an extra emphasis on starting, stopping, touching the ball, and making short passes. My legs began to regain their strength and quickness during these intense sessions, and my stamina slowly returned as well.

The other benefit the broadcasting job gave me was the appreciation that I might possibly make a living at this and the recognition that there were other stimulating things to do that I would enjoy. As it turned out, my foray into broadcasting helped me develop public speaking skills that I continue to use today when talking to all kinds of audiences, ranging from motivational speaking engagements for major corporations to doctor and nursing groups at different healthcare conferences.

BIG BERTHA

As I gained weight and felt better and better, Phil pushed me even harder during our daily workouts. There was hardly a day in which we didn't lift weights, run and sprint, or do something physical. We did nearly all of our running at the Chargers practice fields or in San Diego Stadium, developing what we called "The Course."

The Course was a torturous twenty-five-minute run that consisted of running up and down virtually every step, ramp, and escalator inside or around the cavernous stadium.

One particularly long escalator that rose from the stadium entrance to the upper deck was dubbed "Big Bertha" by the players. She shot up nearly six stories and had ninety-eight steps. I know it was ninety-eight because I counted each step every time we sweated our way to the top. Big Bertha always came at the end of The Course, which made our run even more difficult because we were already exhausted and out of breath by the time we reached her. To make matters worse, the hot sun was usually beating down on us, making Big Bertha that much harder as we sprinted to the top.

Phil always led, gauging how I was doing and pushing me as much as he felt he could. I followed and tried to keep up as best I could, but Phil remembers the day when that all changed:

> It was late May, and we were out for our usual tour of The Course. We started from the locker room, where we always began, and ran up and down a bunch of the steps and ramps at a good clip. By the time we reached Big Bertha, we were really pushing it, sweating hard and fighting for breath.
>
> Until this day, Rolf had always run behind me, letting me set the pace. But on this morning, Rolf surged past me at the base of the long escalator and

said, "It's your turn to follow." I was already exhausted, but I couldn't show it.

We pushed on, further and faster. It was amazing to watch him. I had witnessed his spirit and the strength of his will for months, and now I recognized that his body had recovered and finally caught up. From that moment, I was sure that Rolf would make it all the way back.

By June, I was back to my old self, weighing 178 pounds—the most I'd ever weighed—and feeling great all the time. Most people take their health for granted—I know I did at one time—but when you have inflammatory bowel disease (IBD), you feel miserable and are in pain—almost all the time.

With training camp less than a month away, the thought of kicking again captured my thoughts. It had been nearly nine months since I last kicked a football, and I wondered if I could still do it . . . especially with my bags.

When I mentioned what I was thinking to Phil after one of our morning workouts, he looked at me as if I had two heads. "What do you think we've been training so hard for? Of course, you can kick again. Let's get some balls and do it right now."

I didn't share Phil's confidence, but I was curious to find out if I could physically kick again. We grabbed a few balls and headed to the practice field. In my wildest dreams, I had never seriously thought I would be able to kick again and had been preparing myself for a whole different life. But now that I was well and in good shape, the possibility of kicking again was real. I began to get excited.

When we got to the practice field, Phil took a ball, knelt down, and spotted the football about an extra point distance away from the goalposts for my first attempt. I approached the ball with caution, careful not to pull a muscle, and swung my leg. I looked up in amazement as the ball sailed over the crossbar with plenty of height. Phil didn't waste any time and put down another ball. I kicked the football again with the same result.

After a few more successful kicks, Phil moved me back to thirty-five yards. Once again, I made the kick with lots of room to spare. Pretty soon we were back to fifty yards, and the balls were exploding off my foot and clearing the crossbar with ease. I almost couldn't believe it. I could still kick . . . and maybe even better than before because I was now healthy and in really good shape.

As we gathered the balls, I thanked Phil again for all that he had brought me through. Then I asked him, "Do you think the Chargers will give me an opportunity to compete for my job again? Or do you think they've written me off as damaged goods?"

"I don't know," he replied. "We'll just have to wait and see."

Even though neither of us had answers to my questions, I sincerely believed I could kick again in the NFL . . . *if* I was given a chance.

A Happy Camper

Shortly before the start of training camp, I asked for a private audience with Chargers owner Gene Klein. It's unusual for a player to make such a request, but I needed to find out if the team was going to give me a chance to compete for my old job.

When I walked into his spacious office at San Diego Stadium, Mr. Klein motioned for me to have a seat. I got right to the point. "I really appreciate all you've done for me, especially the support you and the team gave me during my illness last season, my time in the hospital, and now allowing me to work out at the facility to get back into shape," I said respectfully. "I had no idea what would happen and never really thought I could play again, but with Phil's help, I'm back in shape and able to kick again. I believe I can play, and I'm here to ask if you will allow me the opportunity to try to earn my job back at training camp. I know there has been a lot of public support for me from the community and I will never forget that, but we both know the team has a great chance to go to the playoffs again and you need a kicker you can count on. I want to be that guy, but only if you will allow me the chance to win my spot back . . . with no special considerations. I'm just asking for a chance."

Mr. Klein leaned back in his chair and nodded.

I pressed on. "I know this might seem a little crazy. The NFL is a very competitive place, and history says that the weak and the sick and the injured are quickly replaced. I also know that nobody has ever played with an ostomy before, but I believe I can."

Mr. Klein thought another moment before replying. "Well, I appreciate you coming in to speak with me," the team owner began. "We've enjoyed having you on the team, and I don't see any reason why you can't continue your career, provided the trainers and team doctors are comfortable you can be protected. As far as having to earn your job back, we wouldn't want it any other way either. I'll meet with Coach Coryell and inform him about our conversation. I appreciate you coming in, and I wish you the best of luck."

With that, I thanked Mr. Klein and floated out of his office with a huge smile on my face. I almost couldn't believe what had just happened. Against all conceivable odds, I had just been given the green light to try to continue my kicking career! Now it was up to me.

When the Chargers opened training camp on July 15, 1980, at UC San Diego, I weighed in at 175 pounds, just a few clicks under my playing weight from two years earlier and raring to go. I knew I was stronger than ever and just needed to prove to the coaches and my teammates I could regain my old form.

From the first days in camp, I was excited to feel the ball jump off my foot. I discovered my range was just as good—actually better—than before my illness.

Special teams coach Wayne Sevier, however, was determined to bring me along slowly. Experience had taught him that it wasn't a good idea to allow any kicker—especially one whose stamina was still suspect—to kick too much in camp.

With Coach Sevier carefully monitoring my on-the-field progress, I was left with several other concerns:

Would my ostomy appliances stay on during the rigorous two-a-day practices, or would they melt off in the summer heat?

Could I find an adequate way to protect my stomas from a hit?

What would it be like taking showers with the guys with my pouches on?

Would my football pants need to be altered in some way to make room for my appliances?

Our equipment manager, Doc Brooks, was a huge help and worked with our trainers to develop two small pads that fit over my stomas. The pads were held in place by an Ace bandage that I wrapped around my waist. The bandage wrapping took a little while getting used to, but it didn't get in the way and before long I forgot I even had it on. Although I didn't relish the thought of getting hit—a rare occurrence in kicking—I felt well-protected just in case. Since my football pants were made of stretchy material and fit fine without any extra tailoring, nothing showed. I was good to go.

Slowly things fell into place, and all of my concerns evaporated. But could I win my job back?

COMPETITION HEATS UP

My placekicking competition in camp was Mike Wood, a big, muscular guy who looked more like a middle linebacker than a kicker. Mike was a good guy and had replaced me the season before and done a great job in relief, going eleven-for-fifteen and hitting every field goal inside 50 yards.

Mike did, however, have a crucial kick blocked in the 17-14 playoff loss to Houston that the Oilers returned for a touchdown. Although the blocked kick wasn't necessarily his fault, coaches have a way of remembering those things, and they probably questioned whether he could get the ball up quickly enough.

Normally, NFL teams have four preseason games, but the Chargers had been picked to play in the Hall of Fame game in Canton, Ohio, the week before the start of the regular exhibition season. Having an extra game to prove myself turned out to be quite a break.

We traveled to Canton in mid-July, and on the morning of our game, the NFL inducted its new Hall of Fame members. Following the ceremony, we were scheduled to play the Green Bay Packers at the adjoining high school field. Unfortunately, the locker rooms were too small to accommodate the 100 players on each team, so we were forced to dress en masse in the basketball gymnasium.

When we left the relative comfort of the air-conditioned building and made the short walk to the field, I could tell it was going to be a hot one. The mid-summer temperature topped 95 degrees, and the hot air was still and humid as a greenhouse. During warm-ups, I was as worried about my appliances not holding up in the sweltering conditions as I was about kicking.

Coach Sevier told me that Mike and I would alternate kicks, with me leading off. In the first quarter, I trotted out for a routine 35-yarder. This was my first kick in almost a year, and I felt like a rookie all over again. In my nervousness, I rushed the kick and watched the ball hit the upright and bounce back onto the field. I was really disappointed and frustrated I had missed, but I was also becoming increasingly concerned about what might be happening to my appliances in the stifling heat.

At halftime, while the team got out of the heat and toweled off in the cool gymnasium, I slipped away to the bathroom. My uniform was drenched in sweat, and I knew that if my appliances were ever going to come off, this would be the time. I unwound the Ace bandage and cautiously checked for leaks. Nothing! Everything was still in place.

With that concern behind me, I concentrated again on football. The second half proved uneventful until the last two minutes. With the score tied 7-7 and the Chargers deep in Packer territory, it looked like I would have an opportunity to kick a game-winning field goal . . . and show everyone that I was all the way back.

Unfortunately, the weather didn't cooperate. The hot sun had given way to thunderclouds, and the sprinkles of rain that had been falling during most of the second half suddenly turned much heavier. Just as the Chargers drive stalled, tremendous claps of thunder shook the earth, and sharp stabs of lightning struck the ground just beyond the stadium.

"Field goal unit!" screamed Coach Sevier over the din. The field goal team slogged onto the field, but just as we were lining up on the ball, I noticed out of the corner of my eye that a handful of players from both benches were sprinting off the field.

"Hey, what's going on?" I yelled at my holder, Ed Luther.

Before Ed could answer, another piercing clap of thunder reverberated through the stadium. The booming sound was quickly followed by a streak of lightning *very* close to the stadium. Immediately, the referee blew his whistle and called time-out. Then he huddled up with the other referees to discuss the situation. As they were conferring, another booming clap of thunder and bolt of lightning, and the fans had seen enough and stampeded for the exits.

Looking over at the benches, we could see players in a full sprint for the locker rooms. Meanwhile, those of us on the field just stood there, not sure what to do.

"What's going on?" one of the players yelled. But before anybody could answer, the refs blew their whistles, waved their hands, and hightailed it for the exits just as the PA announcer came on to explain that the game was being called off.

I couldn't believe it. *No! Not now! Just one more play!* I was about to attempt a kick that would have won the game and been a big step in my comeback, but that wasn't going to happen. I couldn't believe it. What a letdown!

There was good news, however. I knew now that my appliances weren't going to melt off in the heat, which allowed me to focus completely on winning a spot on the team.

THE COMPETITION CONTINUES

My kicking continued to improve throughout training camp, but I missed a couple of kicks that I should have made. I was working hard on getting the timing down with the snapper and holder, but the pressure of kicking head-to-head with Mike was intense.

The competition was finally decided in the second-to-last preseason game against the Los Angeles Rams in Anaheim. In the first quarter, I got off on the right foot when I made a well-kicked 37-yarder that got up over the line very quickly and had plenty of distance.

Just as the first half was about to end, the Chargers faced third-and-long close to midfield. The punting team got set to go in because a field-goal attempt would've been about 55 yards—not a kick Coach Coryell would usually try.

But Coach Sevier, the special teams coach who'd seen my strength and distance improve each week, had a different idea. "What do you think, Rolf? Do you want to give it a try?"

I didn't hesitate. "Coach, I can make this."

When the third-down play ended with an incomplete pass, Coach Sevier didn't hesitate. "Field goal unit! Field goal unit!"

Coach Coryell couldn't believe his ears. "What did he say?" he asked another coach.

But it was too late to change the decision. The field goal unit was already heading onto the field. Fully aware of the enormity of the situation, Ed Luther gave me a calming word, found a good spot, gave me a great hold, and I nailed the kick, sending it 55 yards through the goalposts with room to spare. It was my longest kick ever in a game and was critically important in putting to rest any doubts about my health or leg strength.

As I jogged over to the sidelines grinning from ear to ear, I was mobbed by my teammates. They seemed almost as excited as I was. I caught Phil Tyne's eyes, and when we looked at each other, we both knew that all the hard work, all the Big Berthas, and all those early morning runs had been worth it. I had made it all the way back.

I was a Charger once again.

To the Showers

Once I made the team, I had to jump over one more major hurdle: showering. All throughout training camp, it was simple to keep the exact details of my surgery hidden from most of my teammates. The showers at UCSD's practice facility were individual stalls, so it was easy to shower in relative privacy. But when we broke camp and returned to practicing at San Diego Stadium, things were different. We had an open locker room layout and showering was done in one community shower room. There was no hiding anything, and in a locker room of a professional sports team, everything is fair game to be made fun of.

I knew this day was going to come, but now it was here. As I sat next to my locker, sweaty and tired after our first full-squad workout at the stadium, I was conflicted. *What do I do? Do I jump in and shower with the guys, or do I try to hide my bags? Or should I wait until everyone leaves?*

I had become more and more comfortable with my situation, but I still hadn't really come out and talked about it publicly. Only a handful of players really knew that my life-saving surgeries had left me wearing two bags.

The fact was, however, there really was nothing I could do. I had to take a shower . . . and wouldn't be able to hide my appliances any longer.

As I looked around the locker room, all the players were hustling to get cleaned up and head home. As I was trying to decide what to do, Phil was walking by and noticed I wasn't changing.

"What's the matter?" he asked.

"I don't know how to take a shower."

"What do you mean?"

"What I mean is that nobody has ever seen . . . ."

"Oh, that's what you're worried about." Phil nodded his head in an understanding way. "Rolf, the guys may be curious, but they really could care less about the bags on your side. They just want to know if you can still kick the ball through the goalposts. In fact, I'll bet after these players fully understand all that you've been through, they'll respect your comeback that much more."

"Maybe," I conceded, but I wasn't completely convinced. "In any event, I guess I don't have much choice. I figured this day was coming sooner or later, and now it's finally here."

With that, I peeled off my uniform, wrapped a towel around my waist, took a deep breath, and headed to the community showers. Acting as if nothing was different, I threw my towel over a hook and walked to an open nozzle. As the warm water cascaded over my head and down my naked body, I glanced at the two appliances, hanging off my stomach in all their glory. I knew there was no hiding them now.

Eight or nine guys were in the showers, chatting away. I held my breath, trying to act nonchalant but waiting for someone to say something. Amazingly, nobody seemed to notice—or they chose to keep their comments to themselves. I washed my hair and rinsed off, grabbed my towel, and headed back to my locker.

I was drying off when one of the biggest defensive linemen on the team came over, shaking his head and smiling at me. "Man, I didn't know your surgeries required you to have an ostomy. My grandmother had ostomy surgery ten years ago. I know what you're dealing with. Welcome back." He stuck out his hand to shake mine.

Wow. Taken aback that anyone even knew what an ostomy was caught me completely by surprise. "Thanks, man," I replied appreciatively . . . and I meant it.

That exchange seemed to break the ice, and suddenly a couple of other players approached me, curious about what they had just seen in the showers. They asked questions that would be on anyone's mind:

"What are those?"

"How do they work?"

"Do they hurt?"

After giving a full explanation of what an ostomy was and what the appliances did, one of the players whistled. "Man, you got guts."

"Actually, I'm wearing these because I *don't* have as many guts as I used to," I tried to joke.

Word got around the locker room that it was show-and-tell time. As more players crowded around my dressing stall, team jokester Hank Bauer couldn't resist, "Hey, Rolf, do you have shoes to match those bags?"

There's always one in the bunch . . . but the last hurdle had been cleared. I had been accepted back onto the team, and I couldn't wait for the season to get started.

SEASON-OPENER

The Chargers decided to keep Mike Wood around as insurance to handle the kickoffs, but I was given the place-kicking duties. We opened in Seattle, where I kicked two field goals in a win, and we got off to a fast start. Mike, unfortunately, pulled a groin muscle the next week and was put on injured reserve, leaving me to take over all of the kicking responsibilities.

Although I was strong enough physically and could certainly kick off, the Chargers were still concerned that I might take a hit during a kickoff return. As a result, Coach Coryell issued strict orders for me to head right for the sideline after every kickoff. Under no circumstances was I allowed to stay on the field and try to tackle the return man. In fact, Coryell half-seriously suggested that he would cut me from the team if I disobeyed.

Initially, that decree was tough for me to follow. A kicker's job is not over until the return man is down, and you don't want to leave your team a man short. Each time I ran to the sidelines, I felt frustrated that I was leaving the field while the ball was still in play.

I never knew what our opponents thought of my "L-pattern," but I did learn from a friend on another team that his coach had instructed his players, "Under no circumstances are you to hit or tackle number 6. If Benirschke is going to beat us, he's going to beat us with his leg. We're not going to deliberately try to take him out." That wasn't ordinary talk in the win-at-any-cost world of NFL football, but no one was complaining, especially me.

There was one time, however, that I "forgot" Coach Coryell's directive. We were playing the Kansas City Chiefs, and I booted a deep kickoff and began running off the field like normal. Just before I reached the sideline, the Chiefs' return man broke free and headed up our side of the field. There was nothing between him and the end zone except for me.

Without thinking about the consequences, I remained on the field and launched my body in his way. We collided and were both sent sprawling to the turf. It felt like I had been hit by a runaway freight train, but at least I had kept the Chiefs' runner from scoring a touchdown. The mystified return man thought he had broken clear of his pursuers and couldn't figure out where I had come from.

"He came off the bench!" he screamed at the referees. "He came off the bench!" Meanwhile, my teammates were putting me back together like the scarecrow in *The Wizard of Oz*. After a quick check, although a little dazed, I found I was still in one piece and couldn't help but laugh at what had just happened. Happily, that was the worst mishap during my comeback season.

The Media Finds a Story

My comeback piqued the interest of the media. They had watched my health decline the previous year, knew I had needed several operations, and were amazed I was back playing. When they learned I needed to wear ostomy appliances, they became especially intrigued. Nobody had ever played in the NFL with an ostomy, and the media wanted to talk and write about it.

NFL Today, a Sunday pregame show on NBC, asked the team's PR department if they could do a feature story about my return. Arrangements were made, and one afternoon a producer and a camera crew showed up at practice.

Before we started the interview, I explained off-camera to the producer that while I appreciated the opportunity to talk about my illness, I was still uncomfortable discussing my ostomies. "I'm still learning to live with them," I explained.

"Understood," the producer said. "We'll do whatever you wish." With that, we started the interview.

After thanking everyone for their support and the thousands of cards and letters I had received, I described my ordeal over the last eighteen months and how I had nearly died after surgery. I explained the differences between Crohn's disease and ulcerative colitis, but I added that we still didn't know the cause—or have a cure—for either affliction. I mentioned that the Crohn's & Colitis Foundation of America was doing heroic work, and if anyone out there was battling IBD, they should call the 800-number for more information. I then encouraged people to write me in care of the Chargers if I could help in any way.

"Okay, I think we have enough," the producer said, signaling the end of the interview. He walked over and thanked me for my time. As we talked, the producer casually began asking me about the specifics of my operation. Thinking he was genuinely interested, I shared some of the more graphic details of my ostomy surgery. Little did I know the cameraman, who had taken his camera off his shoulder, was secretly filming me from his hip!

The next Sunday was a home game. As was our custom, the team stayed at a local hotel the night before the game. After our team break-fast, my roommate, punter Jeff West, and I went back to our room to relax for a moment and pack up to leave for the stadium. We flipped on the TV and caught the beginning of *NFL Today*.

"And we'll be right back with the remarkable comeback story of San Diego Chargers kicker Rolf Benirschke," we heard the announcer say.

"Hey, Jeff, let's stay and watch this before heading over to the sta-dium," I said, curious to see how the story would come across on TV. After the commercial break, the segment began with a summary of my short career and illness.

Suddenly, the camera angle changed and I saw myself explicitly describing the intimate details of my ostomy surgery and appliances. I had been snookered! All the things I was trying to work through privately were literally broadcast across the nation. I was stunned and shocked, and feelings of betrayal welled up inside me. I continued to stare at the TV screen in disbelief.

"How could they do this?" I asked Jeff incredulously. "They knew all that stuff was off the record."

"Amazing, but that's life in the public eye," he consoled.

I was still fuming when I arrived at the stadium. Phil Tyne dropped by my locker.

"Nice interview, Rolf. Way to go."

When I didn't return the comment, he asked, "What's the matter?"

"Phil, that was supposed to be off the record. All that stuff wasn't supposed to be part of the interview."

"What are you talking about?"

"I'm talking about the part where I explained about my ostomy. I wasn't ready to go public like that . . . ."

"So, what's the big deal?" Phil asked. "People know now. That doesn't change who you are. Look at the inspiration you can be for every person with an ostomy. Didn't you tell me there are more than 100,000 ostomy surgeries performed every year? Imagine how those people are going to feel every time they watch you kick a field goal. Imagine how much easier your recovery would have been if you had known someone else who had gone through this before you."

Two days after the broadcast, I received over fifty letters, and the mail kept flowing for weeks. Almost without exception, each letter started: *I'm writing because you're the only other person I know who has gone through what I have.*

Reading those letters blew me away. Phil was right: I had been given an opportunity to jump-start a national discussion about Crohn's disease and ulcerative colitis, two diseases that affect more than 2 million people across the country and the tens of thousands facing ostomy surgery. It was humbling to think about.

After Phil's pep talk, I recognized that the *NFL Today* feature had given me a whole new reason for playing. From that point forward, I decided I wasn't just playing for myself. No, there was a bigger purpose here, a responsibility that I didn't fully grasp until then.

From now on, I would be playing for everyone struggling with inflammatory bowel disease or dealing with an ostomy . . . and that was a huge responsibility.

16

GETTING THE WORD OUT

As the press began asking me more questions and my story reached the public, I discovered that most things about inflammatory bowel disease and ostomy surgery were misunderstood by nearly everyone. In addition, the very nature of its symptoms—fever, nausea, and uncontrollable diarrhea—made the topic difficult for anyone to talk about in public.

Let's face it, nobody wants to stand up in the lunchroom and announce, "Do you know how many times I have to go to the bathroom every day?" Intestinal distress is a real closet illness, seemingly not fit for discussion among family members or friends, let alone with strangers or in the media. But the *NFL Today* ambush turned out to be a blessing in disguise. After that, I figured the word was out, so I began sharing my story as openly and as often as I could.

One of the people who heard about me was Suzanne Rosenthal, the co-founder and president of the Crohn's & Colitis Foundation of America, headquartered in New York City. Suzanne and her husband, Irwin, helped form the organization along with another couple, Bill and Shelby Modell. At the time, Suzanne was battling Crohn's disease, while the Modells had a son also stricken with the illness.

The impetus for starting the CCFA began when Irwin Rosenthal asked his wife's doctor for the names of organizations doing research on IBD. He was told there were none. Zippo! Zilch! Nada!

At the same time, the Modells were asking the same thing of their doctor . . . who happened to be the *same* doctor! That physician encouraged the two families to meet, and out of that get-together came their joint commitment to do everything they could for IBD patients. The non-profit CCFA was born in 1967.

When I happened to mention the CCFA's toll-free number during the *NFL Today* interview, the New York office was flooded with callers. Most of them were patients or their families thrilled to hear someone talk about their disease in public and wanting to learn more. It didn't take long for the CCFA to figure out who prompted those calls.

My visibility remained high because I was kicking for one of the NFL's most exciting teams with Dan Fouts at quarterback and a talented receiving crew headed by Kellen Winslow, John Jefferson, and Charlie Joiner. Our innovative offense developed by Coach Coryell was thrilling to watch. Since we drew huge ratings, the major networks put us on nationally televised games and *Monday Night Football* telecasts as often as they could.

We were also good! All season long during my comeback year, the Chargers were atop the AFC West division. Our final regular season game in 1980 was a Monday Night thriller—at home against the Pittsburgh Steelers. It was a big rematch, and I was symbolically named honorary captain for the game. Incredibly, one of the Steelers' captains that night was running back Rocky Bleier.

As I walked to midfield for the coin toss, I couldn't help but remember reading *The Rocky Bleier Story* a year earlier in my hospital bed as I contemplated my future. I had drawn a lot of encouragement from his gripping story. His NFL football career had to be put on hold when he was drafted into the Vietnam War, where he had gotten shot in the leg and shrapnel seriously injured his foot. Doctors said he'd never play football again, but a tortuous recovery program, months of painful rehabilitation, and great faith and determination had brought him back.

At midfield, I stuck out my hand to the famous running back. "Congratulations, Rocky, for your great career," I said. "Thanks for being such an inspiration to me and to so many others."

We didn't have time to talk further, but after the coin flip, I jogged to the sideline, reflecting on all the past year had brought: *Has it really been only twelve months since that painful walk to midfield with Louie Kelcher the last time the Chargers played the Steelers?* What a difference a year made! I was psyched to kick well, and as it turned out, we needed my four field goals to secure a huge 26-17 victory.

We finished the season at 11-5, and I had my most productive season ever. We beat the Buffalo Bills in the first round of the playoffs, but in the AFC championship game—with the winner advancing to the Super Bowl—we didn't play well and lost a heartbreaker to the hated Oakland Raiders, 34-27.

We honestly felt we had the best team in the NFL that year, which made it doubly tough to watch the Raiders beat up on the Philadelphia Eagles at Super Bowl XV in New Orleans. With the close of the season, however, I realized I had accomplished two important things: I had successfully resumed my NFL kicking career, and I felt great about helping to educate millions of football fans about inflammatory bowel disease.

I was incredibly grateful to be given the chance to play again and really did feel like the luckiest guy in the world. The season's end also brought unexpected awards and recognition. I was named:

- "Hero of the Year" by the NFL Players Association
- "Most Courageous Athlete" by the Philadelphia Sports Writers' Association
- "Headliner of the Year" by the San Diego Press Club
- "NFL Comeback Player of the Year" by *Football Digest*
- "Chargers' Most Inspirational Player" by my teammates

The Associated Press also named me to its All-Pro second team. Later, when network TV decided to bring back Ralph Edwards' *This Is Your Life*, the surprised guest on the premiere show was a stunned but grateful young man—me!

Each time I received an award or recognition of some kind, I couldn't help but think of the many courageous people who were battling IBD alone without a football-crazy city or national audience cheering them on. They were the ones with real courage, and it was humbling and inspiring for me to hear from so many of them.

NEW SWING OF THINGS

Toward the end of my comeback season and almost a year to the day after my own surgery, a professional golfer named Al Geiberger was lying in a Denver hospital bed, recovering from emergency ileostomy surgery for ulcerative colitis. Al had earned the nickname "Mister 59" when he became the first player ever to break 60 in a PGA tournament. On this particular Sunday, however, Al was devastated, believing his golf career was over.

Al was not a model patient. As he was bemoaning his fate to his WOC nurse, the TV set in his room just happened to be tuned to the Chargers game. I had just kicked an extra point when the nurse responded to Al.

"You see that young fellow?" the nurse asked, pointing to the TV. "He has an ostomy just like you, and if he can kick in the National Football League, don't you think you ought to be able to play golf again?"

"Really? What's his name?" Al asked curiously.

"Rolf Benirschke, and when the Chargers were here in Denver last week, he kicked three field goals to beat my Broncos. Would you like to speak with him?"

Al nodded. "Absolutely. Do you know him?"

"No, but I heard him give a talk at a conference, and all of us ostomy nurses across the country love being able to tell our patients about what he has done. His story is really inspirational and demonstrates what a motivated patient can do. The truth is that there are a lot of other amazing stories that never get told but are definitely out there. We know because we take care of those patients every day."

As Al returned to watching the football game, he shared with me later that he began to believe that maybe there *was* life after ostomy surgery. Perhaps he, too, could return to the sport he loved and become another of those inspirational stories that nurses would talk about to their patients.

A short time after Al was released from the hospital, and after connecting with me over several phone calls, we arranged to meet for breakfast at the Torrey Pines Golf Course in La Jolla. I wasn't a golfer at the time, but I certainly knew of Al and what he had accomplished, and that he was often regarded as having one of the smoothest swings on tour. It was fun to trade sports stories, but quickly the conversation turned to the serious discussion about what life would be like for him living with an ostomy. "Do you really think I'll be able to play professional golf again?" he asked curiously.

"Absolutely," I assured him.

"Will the gallery be able to see my appliance through my shirt and pants?"

"Nope," I said. "The gallery will never see it and won't know you're wearing one unless you decide to talk about it."

"What about leaks? Have you ever had an accident?"

"The truth is, every person who wears an ostomy appliance will have an accident at some point, but I played twenty-two games last year, including the preseason and playoffs, and I never once had a problem or a leak. You'll learn how many days—usually four or five—that you can wear your pouch before you need to change it, unless you're in really hot weather or sweating a lot. That's when you may need to adjust and change it sooner," I shared.

Al and I enjoyed getting to know each other and talked for a long time. I know that to be successful in any sport you have to have a strong sense of confidence and self-belief, but there may be no sport that demands that more than golf. There was no doubt in my mind that Al could play again, but now it was up to him. The longer we talked, the more I could almost see the wheels turning in Al's head . . . imagining coming back and competing again.

Sure enough, it wasn't long before Al got himself back into playing shape and made a triumphant return to the PGA tour, amazing all of his fellow competitors and maybe even himself.

Al and I kept in regular phone contact, and one evening, during one of our long conversations, I shared with him the idea of asking ConvaTec, the manufacturer of the pouches we were wearing, to consider using us in testimonial ads to encourage others who were facing ostomy surgery. We jokingly agreed that, if this were to happen, it would be one of the most honest endorsements in sports.

At the time, ConvaTec was a young company in the ostomy

appliance business, but the innovative new product they had developed—that we both wore—served as an especially effective skin barrier and had revolutionized ostomy appliances.

We eventually connected with ConvaTec, and our testimonials had a huge impact. We helped the company develop an instant identity with ostomy nurses and patients across the country. Today, ConvaTec is one of the largest manufacturers of wound and ostomy products in the world and continues to create innovative products to better serve their patients.

As my comeback continued and Al returned to the PGA tour, there was a lot of press about what we had overcome. Whenever articles were written, patients would read them and find a way to contact us. It was heartbreaking to hear many of their stories, but I found that by sharing what we had gone through, we could immediately provide them with hope. And we both learned that hope from someone who had "been there" can be an incredibly powerful force to help patients return to whatever it was they were passionate about.

Hearing from so many patients prompted me to reach out to ConvaTec again with an idea I had been mulling over for a while. I had become increasingly concerned that when my kicking career was over, ostomy discussions would again return to the closet. This concern became the impetus for a program that I developed and called Great Comebacks.

My idea was to find and recognize a new person every year who had successfully overcome ostomy surgery and share that story publicly. I wanted to work with the CCFA in selecting a winner through an application process and then honor that person at the annual Crohn's & Colitis Foundation of America banquet held every June in New York City. The winner would receive a Steuben Crystal Eagle and a three-day, all-expenses-paid trip to the Big Apple. More importantly, a brochure describing their story would educate and encourage others in similar situations.

My dream actually came to fruition, and for three decades now, we've been recognizing inspirational Great Comebacks winners every year. Our website, www.greatcomebacks.com, has been instrumental in educating, inspiring, and connecting ostomy patients as well as being a resource for their families and nurses.

A Different Way of Doing Things

What was also on my mind after my comeback season was investigating several new surgical options that were just being developed.

One of the new procedures involved slicing and re-stitching the end of a patient's small bowel and creating an internal reservoir called a Kock Pouch that would eliminate the need for an appliance. Even though I had adapted well to my appliances and was doing everything I had done prior to my surgery, I was still at greater risk of injury with an external stoma when kicking for the Chargers. While the idea of having an internal pouch was appealing, Kock pouch surgery was still very new.

I had read as much as I could about the procedure and discovered that it was only available for people with ulcerative colitis. The Kock pouch wasn't recommended for those with Crohn's disease because of the strong likelihood that the disease would come back, many times within the walls of the pouch. If this were to happen, the pouch would have to be surgically removed, compounding the patient's troubles. The patient would have to return to a conventional ileostomy, but because of the additional bowel loss, he or she would risk developing "short bowel syndrome," meaning too little intestine would be left to properly absorb nutrients.

Ever since my first operation, when my father looked into the microscope at my diseased colon, he had believed that I was suffering from ulcerative colitis, not Crohn's disease. Others, however, including my gastrointestinal doctor, believed I had Crohn's disease and that had been the official diagnosis.

Although Dad was regarded as one the nation's top pathologists, he was not a GI specialist and wanted other opinions, so he sent slides of my diseased colon to experts around the country. We found it interesting that each doctor came back with a diagnosis "strongly in favor" of ulcerative colitis, but no doctor was willing to say he or she was 100 percent sure. A few specialists claimed the symptomatic and radiological evidence were inconclusive. I have since learned that doctors have difficulty making an exact diagnosis in about 10 percent of patients with inflammatory bowel disease, suggesting that there may actually be another form of the illness.

Still, I was hoping that I'd be in the other 90 percent, so I decided right after the 1980 season to find out if I was a possible candidate for a Kock pouch.

One of the leading hospitals where continent ileostomies were being performed at the time was the famed Mayo Clinic in Rochester, Minnesota. When the Chargers' season ended with our playoff loss to the Raiders, I quickly set up an appointment with a surgeon at the Mayo Clinic, and in the dead of winter, I flew to Rochester to undergo a week of extensive tests to see if they could determine whether I had ulcerative colitis or Crohn's disease. If I had the former, the surgeon had agreed to operate and give me an internal pouch immediately. That way, I would have time to get back in shape before training camp in July and play the next season.

I must admit that I wasn't looking forward to another round of medical tests, but the thought of waving goodbye to two poorly placed stomas brightened my attitude.

Unfortunately, the trip turned into a bad nightmare when a young roommate I had been assigned to in the hospital died unexpectedly during the first night of my stay. I was really shaken up and had a hard time processing what had just happened. To make matters worse, the inconclusive results from my week of tests left my wary doctor unsure of which disease I was actually suffering from. Because he was undecided, he was unwilling to perform the Kock pouch surgery I had hoped for. I returned home shaken and discouraged.

I played the 1981 season with my stomas and bags tucked underneath my uniform but always careful to protect myself when on the field. I had another strong year, highlighted by my overtime field goal that beat the Miami Dolphins 41-38 in the "Epic in Miami" playoff thriller that is still considered one of the greatest games in NFL history. Unfortunately, we had to turn around one week later and travel to Cincinnati, Ohio, to play the AFC Championship game in what would be called the "Freezer Bowl."

The air temperature was -9 degrees Fahrenheit when the game between the Chargers and Bengals started, but with the wind chill factored in, the temperature was -59 degrees, the coldest game in recorded history! The game began with seven operational TV cameras and ended with just two. Several people were reported to have died in the stands due to the incredibly cold and dangerous conditions, and our quarterback, Dan Fouts, still complains of frostbite in the fingers of his exposed hands.

Today, the Freezer Bowl would never have been played—too dangerous. But back then, no alternative protocols were in place, so the game went off as scheduled. Unfortunately for us, we lost the coin flip and the Bengals elected to take the wind and quickly scored 17 points in the first quarter. We were unable to do anything offensively against the cold and strong wind and eventually lost 27-7, prematurely ending our Super Bowl hopes once again. It was a bitter disappointment that still haunts all of us today.

HEADING EAST

During the 1981 season, despite what the Mayo Clinic doctor had said, I hadn't lost all hope of getting a Kock pouch. Dad and I continued to do research and heard good things about Dr. Irwin Gelernt, an experienced colon-rectal surgeon based at Mt. Sinai Hospital in New York City.

Dr. Gelernt headed a group that had become one of the preeminent colon and rectal surgery practices in the country. More importantly, Dr. Gelernt had the reputation of being one of the best Kock pouch surgeons in the world, having trained in Sweden under Dr. Nils Kock himself.

I tracked down his number and called Dr. Gelernt. He was gracious on the phone while I quickly brought him up to speed on my complicated medical history, including the increasing amounts of blood I was seeing in my mucous fistula colostomy, the appliance that was connected to the colon I still had remaining. I felt instantly comfortable with him and was excited to connect with such a well-known surgeon, although my new concern was evident.

"What do you think the blood means?" I asked, getting right to the point.

"It's clear to me that active disease has returned to your colon," he replied.

That didn't sound good. "Which means . . . ."

"You should have the colon removed." His voice didn't hesitate.

I didn't want to go there. "What about a Kock pouch? Is that a possibility?"

"A Kock pouch could work in your situation, but I will need to review your medical records and examine you in person first," he said cautiously. "Since the Mayo Clinic tests were inconclusive, I want to be careful about raising your hopes. If you can come to New York as soon as your season is over, we can take a look and make some definitive decisions. If you're a good candidate for a Kock pouch, there's no reason we can't do the surgery right away. If so, you should plan on staying in New York for approximately one month—two weeks in the hospital and one to two weeks as an outpatient."

The bleeding continued during the rest of the season. Although it didn't impact my ability to kick a football, the loss of blood sapped my energy and caused me to lose a little weight. What was becoming clear to Dad, Mom, and myself was that Dr. Gelernt was right: I would need a surgical procedure—called a colectomy—to remove my remaining large intestine.

The colectomy was scheduled for the week after the season ended to give me as much time as possible to heal and get back in shape. Unfortunately, our run in the playoffs pushed the surgery further back, which was beginning to concern me.

A week after I warmed up from the Freezer Bowl debacle and got over the heartbreak of our disappointing loss, I packed my bags and flew to New York for my operation. I knew it was going to be a difficult and painful surgery as it required slicing my abdomen open from top to bottom one more time. The only ray of sunshine was that the procedure would, hopefully, allow Dr. Gelernt to determine once and for all if I was a Kock pouch candidate.

My first day in New York was spent with some friends from the CCFA. I had been doing volunteer work for the foundation for more than a year now, and the meeting was good medicine. It also gave me a chance to see Suzanne Rosenthal again. Since she knew Dr. Gelernt well—and had even been operated on by him—she reassured me I was being treated by one of the very best.

After the meeting, Suzanne offered to help check me into Mt. Sinai, so we grabbed a cab and headed for the hospital, located on the Upper East Side of Manhattan on 99th and Fifth Avenue. Mt. Sinai was certainly different from any hospital I had been in before. The place was a huge maze of corridors, but what struck me most was the number of blue-uniformed policemen in the lobby. Ah, New York, New York.

An orderly escorted me to the tenth-floor wing, where I would spend the next couple of weeks. While walking down the linoleum-floored hall, I was assaulted by the smells . . . the frantic pace . . . the people in wheelchairs . . . patients on gurneys . . . dozens of medical personnel in white coats and white dresses—scenes that brought back vivid memories of my previous hospital experiences. They were not good memories, and I found myself getting anxious.

I was relieved to reach the relative calmness of my room in the Klingenstein Pavilion wing of the hospital. After I unpacked what few clothes and belongings I had brought along, I pulled open the curtain on the window and found I had a wonderful view of Central Park—a frozen landscape dotted by leafless, barren trees that were gray in the late afternoon light. But with the view also came the sounds of the Big Apple—belching buses, honking cabs, and cars accelerating from the traffic light just up the street.

The scouting report on Mt. Sinai was that it was a great hospital with good people, but that the facility was terribly understaffed. I was tipped off that the only way to insure proper attention was to hire full-time, round-the-clock, private-duty nurses. Because I was facing major surgery and knew there was always the chance of complications, my parents and I decided I would need that kind of care, especially the first week after surgery. They were really kind and picked up the cost for this.

Since my sister, Ingrid, lived in Manhattan, I knew she would visit me as much as she could, as would my new friends from the CCFA— including the Modells and Rosenthals. But the biggest comfort was knowing Mom would be flying out for my surgery.

While I was getting settled, Dr. Gelernt dropped by to introduce himself. Well-known surgeons have a reputation for being big personalities and sometimes difficult, but that stereotype couldn't be further from the truth with this man. Gentle and quick to smile, he was comfortable with himself and a good listener. Perhaps his understanding of what I was about to go through was made easier by the fact that he had recently undergone major heart-bypass surgery himself. It didn't hurt that he was a big football fan who lived and died with the New York Giants. Back in the early '80s, long before the Eli Manning years, he didn't have much to cheer about.

Dr. Gelernt explained that I would undergo two days of tests, followed by surgery early on the third morning. The tests went fine, and the night before the colectomy, I was visited by an anesthesiologist and given a full rundown of what would take place the following morning.

"There is one additional thing I need to tell you," the anesthesiologist explained before he left. "Because this is a rather extensive surgery and involves cutting in a delicate area, there is a 5 percent chance you could become impotent following the procedure."

"Wait a minute," I interrupted with shock clearly etched across my face. "I'm only twenty-six, and that's 5 percent too high!"

He smiled knowingly. "I'm required to tell you that, but actually most of these problems occur in much older men. You should be okay."

"Easy for you to say." I shook my head skeptically.

When he left the room, I couldn't get my mind off that 5 percent. Having been raised in a physician's family, I knew only too well that bad things can happen during surgery, no matter how routine. I had also learned that life doesn't come with any guarantees. That night I spent quite a bit of time praying and reliving all that I had been through. I knew I was lucky to be alive and very fortunate to be back playing football again. I reminded myself that God had a plan for my life and would be there to help get me through this, too, no matter what happened.

I managed to get a little sleep before being awakened at 6 a.m. by the anesthesiologist. I was given an oral tranquilizer and an injection to relax me. By the time I was wheeled into the operating room, I was pretty woozy, but I recall telling Dr. Gelernt that I didn't want to remember any of this.

I didn't.

The next thing I knew, a nurse was gently shaking me and asking me in a loud voice to wake up. The lights were very bright, and as I slowly came to, I heard someone inquire, "How are you feeling?"

"Okay, but when are you going to get started?" I was clearly confused. Then I heard the voice of Dr. Gelernt.

"We're done, Rolf. It's all over. Everything came out great. You're in the recovery room now."

I smiled with relief.

Any kind of abdominal surgery is painful, and this operation was no different. I knew the week after the procedure wouldn't be easy, and it wasn't. The staff was great about getting me Demerol and morphine for the pain when I needed it, although the medications prompted hallucinations as I faded in and out of consciousness.

It was a tough first week, and I was glad Mom was there to get me through the worst. She had been a nurse herself when she first met Dad, so she knew what she was doing when she helped me get out of bed and assisted me during the short walks I was required to take. She also made sure I used the blow bottle by my bed to expand my lungs and help keep me from getting pneumonia. Together with my private duty nurses, I got great care and peace of mind that allowed me to focus on my recovery.

During my awake times, I was relatively coherent, even taking phone calls and carrying on reasonably intelligent conversations. Later though, when asked about them, I couldn't remember much of anything I had said. Perhaps it was a combination of the medication and the mind's way of blocking out pain and unpleasant experiences.

On the seventh day after surgery—February 7, 1982, which happened to be my 27th birthday—the nasal gastric (or NG tube that's inserted through the nose and into the stomach) was removed, which might've been the best present ever.

The NG tube is taken out when the physician feels your bowels are functioning again on their own. This time, however, my NG tube was taken out prematurely. Several hours later, I began throwing up the few bites of Jell-O and crackers that I had just eaten. Vomiting was excruciatingly painful for my sliced-open abdomen, and I became worried that my heaving might reopen the foot-long incision.

Fortunately, that didn't happen, but the NG tube would have to be put back in again, this time while I was conscious. (Normally, the NG tube is inserted at the end of surgery while the patient is still anesthetized.) That was no fun!

Shortly after the awful reinsertion procedure, Dr. Gelernt walked in with a big smile on his face. I couldn't understand his glee, particularly after what I had just gone through. He didn't leave much time to wonder.

"I have some very good news," he began. "Analysis of your removed colon convinces us that you don't have Crohn's disease. You *had* ulcerative colitis. You are now cured. I also moved your stoma to your left side so it will be easier to kick. And if you're still interested, I believe you are definitely a candidate for a Kock pouch. We could do that operation after next season once we see how things go."

What awesome news! I closed my eyes to fight back the tears. My father's hunch had proven to be correct. For more than three years, I had lived with the uncertainty of Crohn's disease, wondering if this type of inflammatory bowel disease would come back and interrupt my life and football career again. But now Dr. Gelernt was telling me that the threat was gone.

Lying in my hospital bed, I couldn't help thinking of the 1.5 million people who weren't as fortunate as me. I looked around the room, filled with flowers and cards. I looked at Mom, sitting there with tears running down her cheeks but smiling as well. At that moment, I made a conscious decision—a promise to God—that I would continue to work with the CCFA and other groups to find the cause of ulcerative colitis and Crohn's disease and encourage others who were struggling with ostomy surgery.

Thankfully, that was not an idle promise, one made during a moment of great emotion. More than thirty years have elapsed since that afternoon, and my life has been greatly enriched as a result of working with people suffering from inflammatory bowel disease, their

I was shocked to receive a surprise call from then-Vice President George Bush, whose youngest son, Marvin, had just undergone ostomy surgery. It was a treat to be invited to the Vice President's residence in Washington, D.C., and meet Barbara Bush, Marvin, and his wife, Margaret, and encourage the family during their difficult time.

Several years later, when George Bush became President of the United States, I had a chance to visit the Oval Office with Great Comebacks winner Irene Fine of Russia.

In 1989, several years after retiring from the NFL, my life took an interesting detour when I became the host of *Wheel of Fortune* with Vanna White.

Looking young and dapper in my NBC publicity photo and trading laughs with Johnny Carson on *The Tonight Show.*

The greatest day of my life was getting married to Mary Michaletz on February 24, 1990.

Before kids came along, Mary and I enjoyed a special trip to Europe that included a few wonderful days watching tennis at Wimbledon.

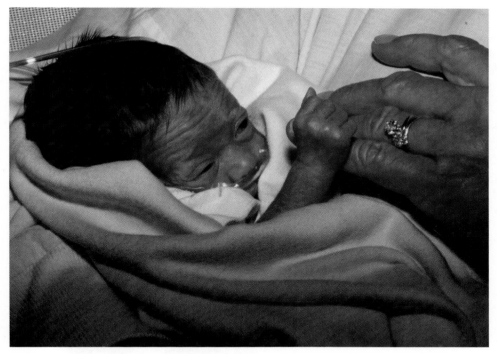

Our daughter, Kari, was born on November 17, 1992, thirteen weeks premature and weighing just over two pounds. She spent two-and-a-half months in the hospital, but a year later we enjoyed a sunset together on a scuba-diving trip to Palau in the South Pacific.

After numerous miscarriages, Mary and I traveled overseas to Russia to adopt brothers Erik and Timmy, ages five and two-and-a-half, respectively, in 1996.

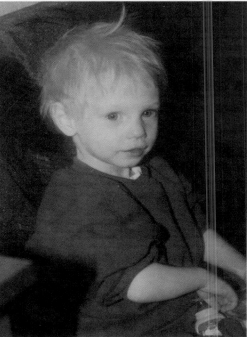

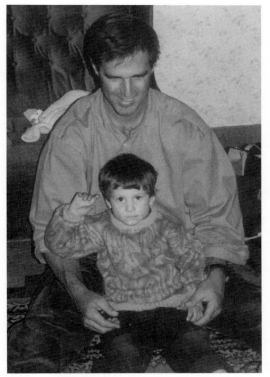

Getting to know Erik in the orphanage.

Taking a walk with tiny Timmy in front of an old Russian church.

It didn't take long for Erik and Timmy to put on weight and connect with their new sister, Kari.

Adventures with the family: an RV trip up the California coast; fishing in Colorado; and visiting Disney World in Orlando, Florida.

In 2006, we moved to Park City, Utah, for a year and made a lot of memories including a trip to Yellowstone National Park and Old Faithful.

This is our Christmas photo from 2009.

When I married Mary, I was lucky to gain five wonderful sisters-in-laws: Julie, Kelly, Joni, and Karen (back row) and Terri (front row), next to my wife.

Our family photo from 2013.

On safari in Africa with Ryan, Mary, and Timmy.

A family Segway outing at the San Diego Zoo Safari Park.

Chargers Alumni Day with old teammates, and remembering old times together.

The San Diego Chargers Blood Drive was started in 1979 to replace the large amount of blood I required for my surgeries. It is annually the largest blood drive in the country and continues thirty-six years later. Here I'm with former Chargers kickers Nick Novak (far left) and John Carney along with Susie Spanos, wife of Chargers owner Dean Spanos, and a fan donating blood.

In 1998, I was stunned to discover that I had received blood tainted with the hepatitis C virus during my ostomy surgeries in 1979. I would need to endure three yearlong difficult courses of treatment before finally getting rid of the virus in 2006.

I've been married to Mary for more than twenty-five years and find myself more in love with her every day. I am a lucky man!

families, and the doctors and nurses who take care of them.

The next few days in the hospital were a painful struggle, but when my intestines finally began working, the doctors removed the NG tube again. This time there were no complications. My body was on the mend. I couldn't wait to get home to San Diego and start getting back into shape.

The night before I was discharged, the two Modell boys, Michael and Mitchell, surprised me with a special going-away present. They knew how much I had missed ordinary food and decided to do something about it. With one of the boys distracting the floor nurse, the other quietly snuck a piping hot pepperoni pizza into my room and closed the door. We laughed and giggled like little kids as we shared the first real food I had eaten in fifteen days.

What a memorable evening. Even though I couldn't eat a lot, I was touched by their kindness, and my taste buds loved every tasty bite of a genuine New York pizza. Eating take-out turned out to be a good test. My system handled everything without any problems, so I knew I was getting better.

Although I lost about twenty pounds during my stay at Mt. Sinai, I was confident I had time to recover and that my conditioning program with Phil Tyne would put weight back on quickly. I set my goal on being ready for the start of Chargers' training camp in July.

Oh, remember the 5 percent chance of impotency I was worried about?

Turned out not to be a problem.

17

THIS TIME,
A SURGERY TO ANTICIPATE

The 1982 football season was one the NFL would like to forget.

The players went out on an eight-week strike and threatened to end the season over lack of true free agency, better pensions, and the chance to share in the huge revenue increases the league was experiencing. Fortunately, both sides finally came to their senses, resolved some of their differences, and we played a shortened schedule. The Chargers managed to qualify for the NFL playoffs for a fourth straight season, but the Dolphins exacted a measure of revenge for our dramatic overtime playoff victory the previous year. They beat us soundly in Miami to end our season.

Personally, I had a satisfying year despite shattering my wrist while playing tennis just three days before the strike was resolved. I needed two pins and a cast to set the break, and then I was forced to wear a huge wraparound pad each game before the refs would allow me to play.

I was lucky not to miss a game and actually earned my first trip to the Pro Bowl in Hawaii. The recognition was the culmination of a dream every NFL player has, but in my case, the post-season honor brought along trepidation. Once again, I would have to shower with a bunch of new players who had only a vague idea of what I had been through. And I'm talking about Jack Lambert, Mike Webster, and Donnie Shell—all legendary Pittsburgh Steelers tough guys—as well as Ted Hendricks and Lester Hayes from the Raiders. It wasn't something I was looking forward to, but I found that my fears were unfounded.

The Pro Bowl players understood—or didn't seem to care—and didn't make a big deal about my ostomy bags.

During our week in the Islands, the players were wined, dined, and entertained by everyone from the governor of Hawaii to network and league officials. The whole experience was very special, but I was glad when the Pro Bowl week was finally over. Ever since Dr. Gelernt had decided a year earlier that I was a candidate for Kock pouch surgery, I had planned on having the operation immediately after my last game. Being selected for the 1983 Pro Bowl prolonged my season by three weeks, however, so I was anxious to get on with things.

Following the game, I decided to stay a few extra days in Hawaii to mentally prepare for what I hoped would be my final major abdominal surgery. I spent time reflecting on the past four years, being ill with inflammatory bowel disease and dealing with the uncertainty of my situation. I had suffered a lot, and my once-sound body was now permanently scarred. I had been forced to deal with the possibility of dying at a young age, never playing football again, and wondering if I would ever marry. I had come to really appreciate the notion that each day is a special gift, dreams can come true, and prayers do get answered.

Finally, I had learned that there was nothing more special than relationships, first with God and then with family and friends. Although my family and I weren't the best at expressing our love for one another, our devotion and concern for each other came out strongly during our time of crisis. Although it's hard to express the depth of my feelings for my mom and dad and brother and sister, I will never forget how they responded when it counted.

I had made many special friends, too, who were there when I really needed them—friends who wouldn't let me give up, feel sorry for myself, or let me shut myself in. Friends I could be totally honest with about my hopes and fears. Friends I could lean on when I didn't think I could go on any further.

ON TO THE BIG APPLE

I celebrated my 28th birthday lying on the warm sands of Waikiki Beach, enjoying the warm tropical breezes but knowing that in a few days I would be lying on the cold steel of an operating table at Mt. Sinai Hospital in New York City. If all went as planned, I would wake up with a Kock pouch.

Dr. Gelernt, who had done my colectomy surgery a year earlier, would be the man in charge once again. I was hoping for a Pro Bowl performance from him.

I was really psyched about going under the knife, but I knew this last hurdle would be a big one. Kock pouch surgery in itself isn't life-threatening, but it's no day at the beach either. I would be sedated for hours, and my abdomen would once again be cut open with a foot-long vertical incision. Constructing the internal pouch is quite delicate and complicated, which is why I was traveling all the way to New York City to be operated on by Dr. Gelernt.

As it turned out, the Mount Sinai surgeon did a masterful job. Everything went just as planned, and I was home within a month, experiencing only a few of the postoperative problems I had been warned about.

Over the next few months, I carefully controlled my intubating schedule as instructed, and the pouch slowly expanded to capacity. By the time training camp came around in July, I was completely healthy and ready to resume my kicking duties with the Chargers.

BOOTED OUT

I continued to play football for four more years following my Kock pouch surgery, but it was increasingly clear with each season that the best days of Air Coryell were behind us. Our success spawned contract disputes and numerous trades. In the mid-1980s, the Chargers were a team in transition—and in trouble. Owner Gene Klein lost his heart for the game, and he sold the club in 1984 to Alex Spanos, a successful real estate developer from Stockton, California.

The team slipped further into disarray, and by 1986, Coach Coryell was asked to "resign" mid-season. Al Saunders was named to replace him, and we finished the 1986 season with a disappointing 4-12 record.

It was clear that Spanos, a businessman not accustomed to losing, wouldn't stand for things as they were and wanted to put his own personal stamp on the team. Change was inevitable, but the way things were revamped wounded many of us in the organization.

As I sorted through my feelings, I recognized that although life as an NFL kicker was a thrilling ride, I also knew it was time to begin seriously thinking about life after pro football. I had far surpassed the average 3.1-year career of an NFL player and knew there was more out there for me to do. At the same time, however, I was just like most other pro athletes who find it difficult to step away from a game they love and had given so much to.

From the first day of the 1987 training camp, it was apparent my relationship with the Chargers would be ending soon. Equally apparent was that the team wasn't sure how to get rid of me. I was still a good kicker, and over ten years, I had become the Chargers' all-time leading scorer, the third-most accurate kicker in NFL history, and one of the more popular and recognizable players on the team.

Despite my past success, the Chargers brought in several kickers to compete for my job, including journeyman Vince Abbott. This was nothing new: every incumbent kicker expects preseason competition. What was different was that no matter how well I kicked, I was never allowed to attempt a field goal during the exhibition games. As the preseason began to wind down, it became clear that I wasn't being given an opportunity to really compete for my job. The fans and the media knew something was up.

Finally, with the media clamoring for an explanation, the Chargers orchestrated a trade to the Dallas Cowboys a week before the final preseason game. I was devastated. I knew in my heart that I could still kick, but I felt like a pawn being moved around the NFL chessboard. Even though I kicked really well in the final preseason game as a Cowboy, the die was cast: Dallas wasn't going to keep me. They had already made up their minds to go with a younger—and cheaper—kicker. The deal between San Diego and Dallas appeared to be a graceful way for the Chargers to extricate themselves from a uncomfortable position.

Although terribly hurt and unsure of what I would do next, in a way I was relieved when I was called into Coach Tom Landry's office and given my release. Although several teams called within a short time, asking me to consider playing for them, I decided my playing career was over. I wanted to remain in San Diego and to always be remembered as a Charger. Besides, I was anxious and excited to get started on the next chapter in my life.

Along Came Mary

Just before the Chargers shipped me off to Dallas, though, something happened that August that would change my life forever . . . I just didn't realize it at the time.

It all began at an outdoor street carnival in La Jolla on a Sunday afternoon just before we had to return to camp for meetings and curfew following our third preseason game the night before. I was walking with Jill, my girlfriend at the time, enjoying the day off from training camp. As we strolled along the streets, we ran into a group of friends and stopped to chat. One of them introduced me to Mary Michaletz, a speech pathologist with a practice in San Diego. She worked primarily with children, she said.

As we made small talk, we discovered that I knew one of her patients, a young twelve-year old girl I had visited in the hospital every Monday for months. She had fallen off a horse and suffered a head injury that required Mary's help to teach her how to speak again. I was stunned at the odds of this happening while appreciating Mary's beautiful smile, winsome attitude, and her lithe, trim figure. But more than that, I was intrigued by her kindness.

In one of those twists of fate, Jill excused herself to find a restroom, leaving me with my friends and new acquaintance, Mary. As the minutes passed, I became more taken with the way Mary interacted with everybody and how comfortable she appeared to be with herself.

When Jill returned, our conversation ended and our two groups went our separate ways. I really went a different way; when, in the following week I was traded to Dallas . . . and was soon out of football. Jill and I broke up not long after that.

No longer kicking in the NFL gave me a lot of time to think about things, and I found my thoughts kept coming back to Mary, the young woman I had talked to for only a few minutes.

On a whim, I decided to see if I could find her number in the phone book in those pre-Google days. I remembered that she was a speech pathologist and figured there couldn't be that many in San Diego. Sure enough, I found her listed in the Yellow Pages. It took me several days to muster up the courage to call her, but when I finally did, I asked her out to dinner.

She was hesitant to accept at first; after all, my call was completely out of the blue, and it had been more than a month since we had first met. But after talking for a while, she decided to take a chance and see what this persistant guy was all about.

We decided to drive up the coast to a quiet dinner spot overlooking the Dana Point harbor. The fifty-minute drive could have been awkward, but we found that conversation came easily. The meal was wonderful, and it wasn't long before it seemed like we were the only two people in the world. .

The ride back to San Diego was different. I realized very quickly I was falling in love, and I knew I would have to tell her about my ostomy at some point. Mary sensed something was wrong.

"What is it?" she asked cautiously. "Just a few minutes ago we were having a great time, and now it's like you're afraid to talk to me."

"I guess I am," I replied tentatively. "You see, I have something to tell you. I was very sick a few years ago, and I needed several major surgeries to save my life. The surgeries left me different than most people."

"What happened?" Mary asked curiously. "As far as I can tell, you seem pretty normal to me."

"Well, I'm not exactly normal anymore." I struggled with what to say next. This was it. The moment of truth. The moment I had worried about ever since my first operation.

By now, however, I had learned that most people took their cues from me. If I was comfortable with the situation, then they could become comfortable as well. Besides, I had no choice. I had to be absolutely honest. There was no bluffing or hiding this. I decided telling her would be better sooner than later. That way, I reasoned, if she decided she couldn't deal with my ostomy, we could nip our relationship in the bud and saying goodbye wouldn't hurt as much.

With these thoughts in mind, I began to tell Mary my story. The whole story. I talked about waking up with two ostomy appliances. About wondering if I would live, and, if I did, whether or not life would be worth living. When I finished, I glanced over and saw she was crying. Big tears were rolling down her cheeks, and she gently touched my arm.

"You're okay now, aren't you?" she whispered. "Does it still hurt?"

"I'm doing fine," I smiled, glad that the truth was out.

We talked the rest of the way home about everything we had both been through, and by the time we arrived back in San Diego and said goodnight, we both knew something special was going on.

Mary and I did fall quickly in love, and we began seeing each other every chance we could. But Mary had a full-time speech Pathology practice and three offices she was running, and I was still trying to figure out what to do with life now that football was over. The transition was tough. I had lost my identity, my income, and self-worth when I left the game. I was reeling. I wondered how I would earn a living and ever replace the structure, camaraderie, and emotional satisfaction of contributing on a team.

I joined a small financial firm with some good friends and began to speak a lot for the Crohn's and Colitis Foundation of America. There were other interesting opportunities, including the chance to host the game show *Wheel of Fortune* with Vanna White (see the next page). But all this uncertainty and change were tough on our relationship. After eighteen months of dating, Mary and I broke up.

A lot of the blame could be placed on my shoulders. The thought of getting married frightened me to death. I didn't have a steady job, was still trying to figure things out, and didn't want to fail at marriage. I wanted to marry just once and knew I wasn't ready, even if Mary was.

Yet, like many other times in my life, something good was going to come out of this extremely painful situation. I just didn't know it at the time.

Give Me a Vowel

I'm an answer to a Trivial Pursuit question: Who took Pat Sajak's place as host of *Wheel of Fortune* back in the 1980s?

Shortly after I retired from the NFL, I was asked by the Crohn's and Colitis Foundation of America to do a small five-city media tour to help raise awareness for the foundation and shed light on a disease that affects millions of Americans.

I was scheduled to appear on *A.M. Los Angeles*, a widely watched Southern California morning television show. I had already done shows like *The Today Show, Good Morning America*, and *The CBS Morning Show*, and I always found the live television experience to be rewarding. Invariably my appearances would prompt hundreds of people to write or call the Crohn's and Colitis Foundation of America and request information, or they would write me to share their struggles and experiences.

But *A.M. Los Angeles* would be different because one of the TV viewers that day was Merv Griffin. Besides being a famous TV personality, he was also the producer of such successful game shows as *Jeopardy!* and *Wheel of Fortune*.

It turned out that Merv Griffin was in the process of developing a new game show and was looking for a host. For some reason, he thought I might be that person and tracked me down to ask if I would be willing to audition. Because I was still trying to figure out what to do next in my life, I said sure. I made several trips to a mock studio in Burbank to learn about the game and try out for the job.

Things took a stranger turn, however, when Merv Griffin called one day and told me that Pat Sajak, the longtime host of *Wheel of Fortune*, had been picked to begin a late-night talk show opposite Johnny Carson and *The Tonight Show*. Because the new talk show was on a competing network, Pat Sajak would have to give up his role hosting the daytime version of *Wheel of Fortune* on NBC. That left Merv Griffin needing a new host. Was I interested?

His offer took me completely by surprise, but then again, I had never thought about playing professional football until I was drafted either. The parallels were not lost on me, so I decided to view this opportunity as an adventure. I thought it would be interesting to get a behind-the-scenes look into an industry I knew nothing about and maybe have some stories to share. At the same time, though, I never thought that trying out as a game show host would amount to anything.

The process of auditioning for *Wheel of Fortune* was a completely new experience for me. I couldn't believe how big the studio was or all the stage hands, makeup artists, cue card holders, cameramen, producers, and stage directors necessary to produce the show. Of course, there was also Vanna White, the letter-turning co-host of *Wheel of Fortune* and one of the most recognizable faces in America.

On the set, I learned that *Wheel of Fortune* was the most-successful game show ever produced, generating hundreds of millions of dollars each year. This show was huge! I also learned that a lot of people were doing everything they could to catch the eye of Merv Griffin and vying to become the next host.

Somehow I got through several auditions and kept getting invited back. After my last audition, I needed to fly to New York for a speaking engagement and to visit my sister, Ingrid. We had a good laugh about me trying out as a "game show host."

"What would Dad think?" Ingrid giggled.

You can imagine my surprise when, upon my return, I found a message on my answering machine explaining that I had been selected as the next daytime host of *Wheel of Fortune*. I couldn't believe it! Me? With Vanna White?

Reality set in the next morning when I was awakened by a phone call from the show's producer. After congratulating me, she explained that we would begin taping three shows on Thursday and then five more on Friday.

"Thursday? You mean in two or three weeks?" I asked.

"No," she replied. "Thursday this week."

Thursday was in three days! Didn't they know that being a game show host was completely new to me? Didn't they realize I had no idea what I was doing? I couldn't admit to the producer that I doubted that I'd ever sat through and watched an entire show of *Wheel of Fortune*. I had no clue how to segue in and out of commercials, read the producer's hand signals, or "follow" one of the four cameras. I was stunned and couldn't completely grasp what was happening. I felt this urge to practice, to train . . . like when I was a rookie trying to earn a spot on the team.

The next few days were crazy. I was besieged by the entertainment media, curious about who I was and why I had been selected. The whole thing became such a circus, and the ruckus reminded me of the locker room at playoff time. Some of the questions I got in interviews were just ridiculous, like the time David Friedman of *Newsday* asked quite seriously if *Wheel of Fortune* was part of my "five-year career plan."

"Are you kidding?" I replied. "I'm trying to get through the next week. But it does feel a little strange being a game show host. Think about it: my father is an internationally known professor of Pathology, a physician, and an author, and his son will be standing fifteen feet away from Vanna White and asking people if they want to buy a vowel!"

When Thursday arrived, I drove up to L.A. feeling anxious and unprepared. As I pulled into the studio parking lot, I found my parking spot next to ones reserved for Johnny Carson and Ed McMahon. Now I *knew* I was in over my head!

Inside the studio, I was introduced again to Vanna White. She was kind and gracious and tried to help ease my nervousness. We were just getting to talk about how this had all come about when the producer dropped in and said it was time for a dry run.

I was amazed at the number of people coordinating the show. I counted at least fifty people doing the sound, lights, and cameras and other things I didn't know much about. During the rehearsal, I made all kinds of rookie mistakes, but I tried to absorb as much as I could. Before I knew what was going on, we began taping shows for real in front of a live audience.

Thus began my six-month stint on *Wheel of Fortune*. Predictably, I became fodder for the *National Enquirer* and other supermarket tabloids. In fact, it didn't take long before I was romantically linked with Vanna. One story gushed that we had an "intimate candlelight dinner" when all we actually did was sit next to each other . . . with the rest of the crew . . . during a catered meal brought in to feed the staff between shows.

I felt especially sorry for Vanna White. Something was always being written about her. Virtually every time we'd tape the show, someone would bring in the latest tabloid with another far-out exposé.

I quickly learned that much of the television industry was driven by fear, not unlike the NFL. Instead of the fear of being waived, it was the fear of being canceled, or the fear of being too old, or the fear of not having the right "look." I found it interesting that some of the biggest celebrities and entertainers I met were also some of the most insecure. They had built their entire self-image on what others thought or wrote about them—or on their overnight ratings.

For me, I had already experienced my sport's "worst fear"—being released from pro football. In the process, I had discovered that life without football wasn't the end of the world. As a result, my attitude about *Wheel of Fortune* was to make sure I did the best I could and enjoy every moment. If the whole thing went away tomorrow, I knew I would survive just fine.

And that's exactly what happened. After six months of doing the show and getting more comfortable with each taping, NBC decided to sell the show to CBS. The new owners wanted to make a lot of changes, including bringing in their own host. My short time in Hollywood was over.

Looking back, I have no regrets. Hosting *Wheel of Fortune* was an interesting experience. I met a lot of great people and made some fun memories, but it was kind of like a detour down a little-traveled side street along the highway of life.

My Andy Warhol-like fifteen minutes of fame were over.

Ending our relationship was difficult for both of us but especially painful for Mary. She insisted that I not call or write, and she even asked me not to go to the same gym or the restaurants we used to frequent together.

We were apart for five months, abiding by the rules we had set for each other when one afternoon, after giving a luncheon talk to a non-profit organization, a close friend of Mary's came up to say hello. I felt awkward chatting with her, but seeing Mary's friend brought back a flood of memories and an overwhelming desire to find out how Mary was. Finally, I couldn't help myself anymore.

"How's Mary?" I asked hesitantly.

"She's fine," responded the friend. "I know she was really hurt when you two broke up, but she's moved on with her life. She's back to dating now."

When we said goodbye, I found I couldn't get Mary out of my mind. Literally every night for the next week I found myself waking up at 2 a.m., thinking about her. I prayed a lot and wondered if God was trying to tell me something. I tried everything to fall back asleep, but nothing worked. Instead, I would just lie there, tossing and turning until daylight when I could finally get dressed and go to work.

After a week, unable to stop thinking about Mary and rapidly losing the ability to function in my sleep-deprived condition, I called her friend back.

"Is Mary in love with anyone?" I asked with some trepidation.

"I'm not sure," came the answer. "But she is seeing someone."

Buoyed by this glimmer of hope, I hung up and immediately tried to call Mary at her office. She wasn't in, but her secretary explained she would be back at 11:45 a.m. and wouldn't have another patient until 1:30 that afternoon.

The time was 11 o'clock. Without thinking about what I was doing but knowing I needed to see Mary, I jumped into my car and headed to her office. Suddenly, it was all very clear to me. I believed I was supposed to marry this girl! We were meant to be together. All of the fear and uncertainty I had been struggling with for the past many months were completely gone. I just knew this is what we were supposed to do . . . now I just needed to convince Mary that I wasn't completely crazy.

I arrived early at Mary's work and begged her secretary not to tell her I was inside waiting when she returned. When Mary stepped into her office and found me sitting there, she was absolutely stunned and shocked. We hadn't seen or talked to each other in over five months, and now here I was in her office. Her face flushed and I could see her getting angry, but before she had a chance to say anything, I tried to apologize for the pain I had caused her.

"Mary, I'm so sorry for the hurt I've caused you," I said with tears in my eyes. "I know it's been hard on you. I know I haven't been easy to be around. But I've taken the last five months to grow up a lot, and I really miss you. I'm ready to get on with my life—to make a commitment to you."

I got down on one knee.

"Will you marry me?"

Mary couldn't believe what was happening.

"Are you kidding me? Don't do this to me," she answered angrily, clearly in shock. "I'm just getting over you. Where is this coming from? Why should things be any different? I don't want to get hurt again."

"Mary, I know that the time we dated was difficult, especially the way it ended, but I also know that we had something special."

"I know, but what about the things we've struggled with?"

"We can work those things out. You know a lot of that was caused by my insecurity and uncertainty about what I was going to do."

Mary was beginning to see that I had changed. I was different, but how could she say yes after not having seen me for more than five months?

"Would you be willing to go see a marriage counselor? Would you be willing to see if we can work out some of our issues?" she asked bluntly.

"Absolutely!" I responded, sensing I was getting somewhere. "Whatever it takes."

Mary was understandably cautious. We went to lunch and talked further and agreed to try counseling. After a few visits, she knew our love for each other was real and that I was sincere in my transformation. Our on-again, off-again romance was on for keeps, and in November 1989, we became officially engaged.

Mary's younger sister Joni—one of five sisters—was already engaged and planning an April 1990 marriage. Since we didn't want to wait until June or July, we asked Joni if she would mind if we got married in February. Both she and her fiancé, Earl, bless their hearts, gave us their approvals, and we rushed to get started.

With only three months to plan the wedding, we found a pastor, a church, and a reception area . . . and exchanged "I do's" on February 24, 1990. It was the happiest day of my life. Being married to Mary has been everything I hoped it would be—and much more.

Little did we know about the challenges that life had waiting for us—challenges that would be exceedingly more difficult than the illness and ostomy surgeries I had gone through previously.

18

IN A FAMILY WAY

Mary and I were ready to start a family as soon as the ink was dry on our marriage certificate. We were both nearing our mid-thirties, so while it wasn't now or never, it certainly felt like we didn't want to waste any time.

Unfortunately, as I had already learned from my illness struggles, life doesn't always work out the way we want it to. That became especially true as we tried to have children. Getting pregnant was not the problem—it was carrying a baby to full term that turned out to be difficult. Mary and I endured three sudden miscarriages and a stillborn child at twenty-five weeks. The miscarriages were incredibly painful losses for us, but even more devastating was when we were told by our doctor that Mary would have to deliver our stillborn baby girl. To watch the heartbreak in Mary was so hard that it's still painful even to write about.

I learned a lot about my extraordinary wife during all of these trials, and what really stood out was her amazing strength. She just would not give up, no matter how difficult the circumstances were. So we tried again, and once again Mary became pregnant. We were told that we would be having a daughter, but given our history of difficult pregnancies, we would be doing things differently this time. Mary did everything her doctor asked her to do—took it easy, got plenty of bed rest, moderated her workouts—but unfortunately, she again developed pre-term labor and our daughter was born thirteen weeks prematurely, weighing in at just over two pounds.

We named her Kari, but immediately doctors told us to prepare for the worst because our daughter was not expected to survive. She had been badly infected with *E. coli* bacteria at birth and had suffered a stroke and a grade four bilateral brain bleed. She was immediately placed in the Neonatal Intensive Care Unit (NICU), where every day became a saga.

For ten weeks, Kari battled for her life inside the NICU, receiving excellent care from the incredible nurses and doctors at UCSD and lots of prayers from a chain of special friends. There were difficult decisions that Mary and I had to make almost daily, testing our faith and endurance. We virtually lived at the NICU, most days only able to look at Kari through her incubator and not even able to hold her until she got a little older. The possibility of a brain shunt became imminent, but continual spinal taps that relieved the pressure building up in her brain ultimately averted that development.

It turned out that Kari was much like her mother: a strong fighter with an enormous heart that just wouldn't quit. As the weeks stretched out and turned into months, our hearts were elated when it became apparent that she was going to survive. Today, Kari is a bright, precious daughter in her early twenties who has a mild case of cerebral palsy in her legs, but she is a blessing that I cannot possibly explain.

Unfortunately, due to the difficult time Mary had during her pregnancy, our doctors told us that she would likely not be able to have any more children. That was extremely difficult for Mary to hear as she came from a family of five sisters and was really looking forward to having more kids. So, trusting the leading from the Lord and feeling a strong desire to raise more little ones, Mary and I began looking into adoption.

We pursued a local adoption first and were put in touch with a young woman in a crisis pregnancy. She agreed that we could adopt her child, and we agreed to support her during her last few months of pregnancy. After the child's birth, we brought an infant girl home from the hospital, but eight days later, the birthmother changed her mind and wanted to keep the baby. Her sudden change of heart nearly crushed us.

While we were still sorting through our emotional hurt, we had the opportunity to hear Pat Williams, the general manager of the Orlando Magic NBA basketball team, share his testimony of adopting thirteen children internationally after having four kids of his own. Mary was particularly touched by his story, so we decided to see what could be done with an international adoption.

We saw God open doors for us to adopt a four-year-old Russian boy named Valery. Unfortunately, just after completing the paperwork, we found ourselves caught in an adoption moratorium, a time when Russia decided to stop all adoptions so they could standardize the procedure. The uncertainty was frustrating, and we agonized over what to do. We wondered if and when Russia would re-open adoptions to westerners.

Seemingly out of the blue, another adoption opportunity became available in San Diego. Unfortunately, after supporting another young lady for three months, she decided to keep her baby at birth, leaving us once more to deal with immeasurable emotional hurt and to ponder what God had in store for us. We didn't have to wait long, however, because just two days later we received a phone call from our Russian contact explaining that the adoption freeze had been lifted and that we were cleared to go over and pick up our little boy as soon as we were able.

Naturally, we were elated, and ten days later I was on a plane to Kaliningrad, a coastal town on the Baltic. We decided it was best to have Mary stay home with our daughter while I traveled with my brother-in-law to pick up young Valery.

When I arrived, we were told by the authorities that Valery had a younger brother named Viktor who had been separated from Valery and was living in another orphanage about an hour-and-a-half from Kaliningrad. We went to visit him in the orphanage and were appalled at his gaunt frame and listless behavior. Viktor was almost two-and-a-half years old, but he weighed only seventeen pounds. I found my heart breaking for this precious young boy but didn't know what we could do.

When I returned to Kaliningrad, however, the Russian authorities made it very clear to me that if I wanted to go through with the adoption of Valery, I would also have to take Viktor.

I had one day to make the decision, so I tried to call Mary to talk about this sudden opportunity. Unfortunately, it was impossible to reach her . . . international phone service was difficult in that part of Russia. This being the mid-1990s, there was no email back then. I was left to discuss my dilemma with my brother-in-law and to pray. For a night, I reflected on all we had been through, how we had gotten here, and the potential consequences of my decision. I was really bummed I couldn't reach Mary, but I felt like God was asking me to trust Him. So with that understanding, I made the decision to bring both kids home.

When all of the paperwork was completed and we flew to Moscow to clear through the U.S. Embassy, I was finally able to call Mary and explain what had happened. You can imagine what an interesting phone call that was when I told her I was bringing *two* boys back instead of one and that she needed to get another crib ready! She was amazing and couldn't have been happier.

Within a few short months, Erik (Valery) and Timothy (Viktor) became an integral part of our family. We learned quickly that routines helped them feel secure and safe, so we began assimilating them into our family's way of doing things—eating meals together, taking baths, reading bedtime stories at night, and going to church.

As we tried to comprehend what our new sons must have been through, we experienced some heart-wrenching behavior. Since we couldn't speak ten words of Russian, we had to resort to sign language and voice tone in order to communicate.

If we said "no" with any kind of authority, the boys would become very upset and run out of the room or cower under a desk or bed in utter terror. In the evening, even if they were exhausted, they wouldn't allow themselves to fall asleep on our shoulders as we tried to rock them to sleep. In the orphanage, they had learned self-preservation strategies that involved not trusting or relying on caregivers who were too often not there when they were cold or wet or scared and needed somebody to help them. The boys, especially Timmy, learned to calm themselves down by vigorously rocking their tired bodies to sleep in their beds. It was hard to watch and imagine what had led them to do this, but they had mastered the behavior and could be asleep in less than a minute.

Erik and Timmy also had an almost unimaginable fear of dogs and would scream hysterically at the sight of even the smallest pooch. We learned later that, as infants lined up in their cribs in the orphanage, large dogs would be allowed to wander around the rooms and sniff and lick the kids through the crib bars. With no ability to get away and no one around to remove these "monsters," they developed an intense phobia for dogs.

From what Mary and I had read about orphaned children, we knew that food would likely be an issue. It was. The first week we discovered that the boys were hoarding leftovers and storing them in secret places. We'd find bread rolls stuffed in their pockets and cookies tucked under their pillows or stashed in the back of their clothes drawers. It was clear these kids had been severely deprived, and, most likely, treated harshly. That knowledge broke our hearts even more.

At times, however, hidden food seemed the least of their past scars. In the first six months, we experienced dozens of tantrums and witnessed angry episodes that seemed to come from nowhere. I would often come home from work and find Mary in tears after a particularly stressful day with the boys. It was during those difficult moments that we leaned on the belief that with lots of love their emotional scars would heal.

Those emotional scars, while significantly better, remain to this day.

STILL YEARNING

As our household finally became more settled, Mary began expressing a desire for adopting a fourth child. Growing up as one of six daughters in the tiny rural community of Green Isle, Minnesota, Mary had always longed for a large family. But with all of the issues we were facing with our three preschoolers, I was hesitant to add another to the mix.

One evening when I wasn't home, Mary happened to catch a segment on a TV newsmagazine show about a new treatment for women who had had multiple miscarriages or who had experienced difficulty carrying a pregnancy to term.

Mary, who had endured the painful loss of three unborn children through miscarriage and a stillborn little girl at twenty-five weeks, watched attentively. Piqued by the segment but not wanting to alarm me, Mary quietly made an appointment to see her OB-GYN and learn more about this new treatment.

After a complete physical, the doctor explained, "Before we can even consider any new therapy, we have to wait until your next period begins." It was while charting her cycle that Mary discovered that she was already pregnant.

"How did that happen?" I joked in disbelief. The shocking news excited us, but it also raised major concerns and brought back painful memories.

Knowing what we were up against, we worked closely with our doctors, who determined that in her sixteenth week she would have a cervical cerclage—a procedure in which the doctor stitches up the opening to the cervix. Following that minor operation, Mary was put on complete bed rest: no cooking, no housecleaning, no exercising of any kind, no playing with the kids, no getting up for *anything* except to go to the bathroom.

Initially Mary resisted, not because she didn't believe the doctor, but because she didn't want to burden others. Fortunately, we had arranged for a young Austrian au pair to join our family even before we discovered Mary was pregnant and would be relegated to the couch for the rest of her pregnancy. Maria arrived in the fall of 1997 just as Mary was forced off her feet. She proved invaluable, and the timing couldn't have been better.

But our new helper couldn't do it all. Word of Mary's condition quickly spread to our friends, who immediately set up a schedule to help take the kids at different times and arrange for hot meals to be delivered five days a week. They must've known our family would never survive on my cooking!

While we were in complete awe at the way our friends pitched in so unselfishly, Mary found it humbling and very difficult to accept kindness that she felt she could never repay. She had always been very active and capable, so she wrestled with the fact that she couldn't do anything but lie on the couch and watch the world go by. She was able to swallow her pride and take on this new challenge, however, when she weighed the possibility of losing the precious child growing inside her. She vowed to make the most of the situation.

Five months of anxious bed rest passed before Mary reached a time when the doctors felt the child could be born without complications. During her thirty-sixth week, after a long and emotional pregnancy filled with daily highs and lows—and celebrated every week she was able to keep the baby—no one was happier than us when the doctor delivered our baby boy by Cesarean section, only four weeks ahead of his due date.

Ryan Joseph Benirschke joined our family on February 12, 1998. With a five-year-old, four-year-old, three-year-old, and now an infant under one roof, life turned even more hectic and stressful in a hurry. A full night's sleep became a distant memory, but we were ecstatic about our new family.

Little did we know that life was about to take another *very* unexpected detour.

19

A Routine Life Insurance Exam

Following the birth of Ryan, I realized that I needed more life insurance. With four children so young, I wanted to make sure Mary was adequately provided for in the event of—to use insurance jargon—my "untimely demise."

Before insurance companies issue a policy, however, they require a medical exam that includes an analysis of blood, urine, and an EKG, plus a thorough review of your health history. I had gone through this several times already and was quite familiar with the process. When the insurance examiner dropped by my office that spring morning to perform his tests and collect the necessary samples, I didn't give his arrival much thought. In my mind, I was in excellent health for someone in his early forties. I loved working out and staying fit, in keeping with a lifestyle that began even before I was playing professional football.

A week later, my doctor surprised me with a call. "Rolf, on your blood test, I noticed that your liver enzymes were slightly elevated. I'd like you to come in and let us see if there is something going on."

I thought nothing of his request as I had seen this kind of discrepancy often with clients over the years. You see, I was working in a financial planning firm at the time where we often coached clients on the importance of having adequate life insurance, even though they might be young and in seemingly good health. I was forty-three years old and in excellent shape, so I was taking my own advice.

Still feeling no sense of urgency but knowing I hadn't had a comprehensive physical since my playing days, I made an appointment with my doctor, Mark Bracker, at UCSD.

As I walked into his office, he didn't appear too surprised to see me.

"Rolf, how's the family?" he asked as he shook my hand. "I know you're not here to make sure you don't have any more kids, but we can work that in too," he said with a chuckle. Dr. Bracker had heard about how we had adopted two boys from Russia and then the somewhat surprising birth of little Ryan, bringing the number of our children to four. "We do our vasectomies on Fridays. Should I schedule you?"

"No," I grinned and brought the conversation back to the issue at hand. "You asked me to come in so we can understand why my liver enzymes are out of the normal range."

A look of concern came over his face as he offered me a seat. "Yes, I think we need to have some more blood drawn," he replied. "I'm going to order some specific liver tests for the lab tech to run. But first, let's have a look at you."

After my examination, Dr. Bracker handed me a lab slip. "Have that blood drawn today if you can," he said. "It will take a few days before we get the results, so I'd like to jump right on this. I'll call you when I learn something."

"Fine," I said. I left the office, glad that I was going to find out what this was all about, but at the same time, I was a little curious at why he was anxious to get things moving so quickly.

It was several days before I heard back from Dr. Bracker. "Rolf, I have the results from your tests. I'd like to see you in my office if possible."

"When do you want me to come in?" I asked a little nervously.

"How about today?" he said. "I have an opening at four o'clock."

He's in a hurry, I thought. "No problem, that will work," I said.

Unlike the previous visit, there was no easygoing smile on his face when I walked into his office. Dr. Bracker didn't waste any time getting right to the point.

"Rolf, how have you been feeling?"

"Great," I said.

"Tired?"

I smiled ruefully. "Doc, with four kids under the age of six, my wife and I are both exhausted *all* the time."

"How's your weight?"

"I've lost a few pounds, but I'm up several times during the night and not able to sleep like I normally do. Besides, I can't seem to find the time to work out regularly as much right now."

"Any abdominal pain?"

"No."

"Rolf, when you had your ostomy surgeries back in 1979, do you remember if you needed any blood transfusions?" he queried.

"Did I need blood?" I responded, rolling my eyes. "I practically don't have any of my own left! Before it was all over, they said I needed close to 80 units of blood and blood products to keep me alive."

Dr. Bracker glanced at his chart and then looked up as he slowly adjusted his glasses. "Rolf, that explains it. It appears you were infected with the hepatitis C virus and got the virus from tainted blood used during your operations."

It was a good thing I was sitting down because the news almost knocked me over. I had read something about hepatitis C and the growing number of people suddenly discovering they had the virus, but that was as far as my knowledge went.

"What does this mean?" I asked hesitantly, not sure if I was going to like what I was about to hear.

"Hepatitis C is a virus that gets into the bloodstream and then attacks the liver. It wasn't formally identified until 1989, and a year later a hepatitis C antibody test was developed. Prior to that, physicians knew there was something out there but didn't have a name for it. They were calling it non-A or non-B hepatitis because it attacked the liver and acted like hepatitis. A more specific test was developed in 1992, and that is when most blood banks and testing facilities began using it to screen their blood. Today, our blood supply is very safe, but before the implementation of that test, about 10 percent of the people who received blood became infected with the virus."

"Are you saying that anyone who had a transfusion prior to 1992 is at risk?" I asked incredulously.

"Yes, but there are other ways to contract the virus. Hepatitis C can be transmitted wherever there is blood-to-blood contact. It doesn't have to be a transfusion. In fact, people who share contaminated needles while doing intravenous drugs spread most hepatitis C. Health-care workers must be on guard against accidental needle sticks while working on an infected patient, and first responders and military personnel need to be careful about blood spatter getting into an open wound. It has also been found that tattoo parlors and body-piercing places can spread the virus through unclean needles and tainted dyes. There is some concern about sexual transmission, although the chances appear to be quite low. People who have been on dialysis are also at risk, as are those who are treated for hemophilia."

I sat in the office, stunned at this frightening news. How could something like this be discovered *twenty years* after the infection had occurred and I not be aware of it? Wasn't the blood I had received supposed to have saved my life and not put me at risk again? I started to get angry. *This just isn't fair*, I thought to myself.

As if reading my mind, the doctor helped bring me back to reality. "Let's try to keep this in perspective. The fact is, it's a small miracle you don't have AIDS. Remember, we weren't testing for HIV back in the late 1970s either, so you could be dead by now."

"Yes, I suppose so," I sighed, still trying to comprehend what this all meant. As we wrapped up our visit, I couldn't help but think that I was about to travel once again down the path less taken. I knew from my previous experience with ulcerative colitis that before I let my imagination run away to the worst possible scenario, I needed to learn more about what I was up against. But that was hard. This news was so shocking and had come so out of the blue that I was finding this latest twist hard to process.

As I left the doctor's office and drove home, little did I know that I was about to embark on an eight-year odyssey filled with physical and emotional challenges, hopes, and heartaches that would affect me and my entire family.

A New Treatment Plan

I wanted to give Mary the news in person. While I was en route to home, I thought it would be a good idea to call my father.

"Hi, Dad," I began. "Listen, I just left Dr. Bracker's office. You're not going to believe this, but I apparently have hepatitis C."

"Oh, no, Rolf," replied my father.

"Dad, what the doctor told me has me scared to death. Do you know much about hepatitis C?" I asked, my voice starting to shake. "I need more information before I tell Mary."

"Actually, I do," he answered, measuring his response carefully. "We just had a briefing for all the medical personnel at the hospital. Apparently, there are vaccines available for hepatitis A and B, and both are quite treatable now. Unfortunately, hepatitis C is a different story altogether. The good news is that new and improving treatment methods are being developed as we speak, but the bad news is that the current therapies are only about 20 percent effective. And I heard that those same treatments also have difficult side effects. What else do you know?" I asked.

"Hepatitis C attacks the liver, initially causing inflammation and fibrosis. If left untreated for ten to twenty years, it can eventually lead to cirrhosis and even liver cancer. Hepatitis C is a huge problem that is just now emerging as the next big health epidemic. It has been called 'the silent killer' and is very serious."

"But Dad, I had no idea I was a carrier. I've been feeling great. Could I really have been infected for almost two decades?"

"Apparently, you can. The difficulty with the virus is that it generally doesn't show any symptoms for a long period of time. It's a good thing you don't drink much because alcohol is very hard on the liver and can accelerate the damage."

I thanked Dad and began thinking how I would break the news to Mary. I decided that before I could, I needed to do some more research on my own.

Late that night, after Mary had gone to bed, I propped myself up in front of my computer and began searching the Internet. I visited a handful of helpful websites, including the Hepatitis Foundation International, the American Liver Foundation, and the Hep C Connection.

The liver, I learned, stores sugar and vitamins and makes bile acids necessary for digestion. The organ serves as a filtering station, removing wastes and poisons from the bloodstream. Since I had had my large colon removed nearly twenty years earlier, my liver was an even more important organ for my digestive system.

I discovered that Dad had been right: Hepatitis C was a serious form of liver disease, affecting 3.5 million Americans as the most common blood-borne infection in the U.S. Today, there are 30,000 new cases diagnosed each year in the U.S. and about 170 million carry the virus worldwide. Even back in the late 1990s, hepatitis C was already the leading cause of liver transplants; these days 4,000 people get new livers each year, while 12,000 other folks are waiting to receive one. Many die before a liver can be found.

As I learned more about this lurking killer, I realized that there had to be hundreds of thousands of people like myself who are totally unaware that they are carrying the hepatitis C virus in their bodies. How many had experimented with drugs in their younger days, even just one time, and become infected? How many had unknowingly received blood transfusions tainted with the hepatitis C virus prior to 1992? I could only imagine.

Whereas inflammatory bowel disease and ostomy surgery are not pleasant subjects to discuss, I discovered that hepatitis C had its own difficulties. Studies indicated almost 40 percent of the people with hepatitis C became infected after participating in some inappropriate activity when they were younger—and not wiser. For someone to volunteer to be tested for hepatitis C, it might mean having to explain their past behavior to a spouse, boss, or friend, so many choose to avoid the potential embarrassment.

And then there are people like me who were the recipients of con-taminated blood during a surgery. It turns out that there are a lot of women who unknowingly received a small amount of blood during a Cesarean section at childbirth. It is only after getting diagnosed with hepatitis C and reexamining their medical records that they learn the fateful truth of how they must have been infected.

On the other hand, my research informed me that many others with hepatitis C can never pinpoint exactly how or when they got the virus. They never participated in "at risk" behaviors or received a transfusion.

The Centers for Disease Control estimates that approximately 40 percent of the infected population falls into this "uncertain" category, their infection remaining a mystery.

The vast majority of people find out they have the virus quite by accident—usually through a routine physical examination. Elevated liver enzymes in the blood are generally the first indicators, although symptoms like fatigue, poor appetite, weight loss, jaundice, appearance of dark urine, fevers, and vomiting may also be early signs. I had not experienced any of these symptoms, except for the fatigue and mild weight loss that I had attributed to sleepless nights with our newborn son, Ryan.

After spending most of the night staring at the computer, I finally headed for bed and a restless few hours of sleep. In the morning Mary rolled over, still half asleep. "Nice of you to return to bed," she said. "Was I kicking you last night?"

"No, Mary. Listen, I have some bad news." I was having a hard time looking her in the eyes.

She sat up quickly, now wide-awake. "What is it?"

"I was up late last night on the computer learning as much as I could about a new health problem."

"What health problem?" I could see the panic rising in her face.

"My health problem. You see, my physical last week confirmed that I am infected with the hepatitis C virus. Apparently, I have been carrying it for almost twenty years. Because you and I share nail clippers, a toothbrush every now and then, and even a razor, there is a chance you could also be infected. I'm so sorry." Tears began to well up in my eyes.

"Oh, Rolf," Mary reached over and squeezed me. "You've been through so much. We're going to be all right."

"I feel so unclean," I sputtered, trying unsuccessfully to control a deep, body-shaking sob. I knew our world had just been altered. I just didn't know by how much.

PLANS FOR THE FUTURE

It took both of us a few days to fully grasp how our lives were going to change living with hepatitis C. As the reality of our situation became clearer, we organized a family meeting with parents, brothers and sisters, and a few close friends to explain what had happened.

The first order of business was learning how far the disease had progressed in my body. Dad and Dr. Bracker suggested that I see Dr. Tarek Hassanein, a hepatologist on the forefront of hepatitis C research at the University of California San Diego (UCSD) campus.

"Rolf, before a treatment can be prescribed, we need to draw some more blood, do an ultrasound, and take a liver biopsy," he explained during my first visit to him.

Great. More blood work, I thought. And just thinking about having a long needle inserted into my side to extract some liver tissue was a frightening prospect.

"Is this going to hurt?" I asked hesitantly, imagining the worst.

"Actually, the liver biopsy has become fairly routine," he replied. "It is very quick and with the new drugs available, you won't remember anything."

Dr. Hassanein was right. With the exception of a little trouble putting an IV line into my arm, the procedure was not difficult. After liver cells were removed and sent to the lab, the severity of the disease was graded. The result: I had beginning stages of fibrosis but I had not progressed to cirrhosis. This was good news since the liver is the one organ that can regenerate itself if it has not become too damaged or scarred.

"Is there a treatment program?" I asked cautiously.

"Well, there are options, Rolf," Dr. Hassanein answered. "The first treatments that were developed were only about 20 percent effective in keeping the virus in what we call a 'sustained viral response.' Lately, however, we are seeing all kinds of new studies being done that have bumped the successful treatment rate to about 40 percent. A lot depends, however, on which genotype of the virus you have, what your viral load is, and how quickly we can get your enzymes back to normal."

"Viral load?" I asked quizzically.

The physician was an expert on hepatitis C, and he must have explained this a thousand times in his practice.

"Viral load is the amount of virus in your blood. We measure in parts per million. If you have a load of less than 2 million, you are considered to have a light load. If you have more than 5 million units, then you have a high viral load. Studies seem to indicate that with a lighter load, we have a greater chance of pushing the virus to an undetectable level. It turns out, you have a light viral load, only about 500,000 ppm."

"Well, finally some good news," I said.

"Oh, there's one more thing," he cautioned. "Any alcohol will injure your liver that much quicker, making it even harder for the organ to replace the damaged cells. You need to stop drinking completely—no beer, no wine, no margaritas. No liquor of any kind."

Actually, there was some more very good news. I was relieved when, after Mary was tested, she was found to be negative for the hepatitis C virus.

THE NEXT STEP

It turns out that Dr. Hassanein was heavily involved with many of the clinical trials that were being done by the various pharmaceutical companies, and he knew several of the new therapies were having good results. I felt comfortable under his care because his mother in Egypt had been infected with the unknown virus, which set him on a course to become a doctor and make hepatitis C his life's work.

Based upon the biopsy results, and the fact that I had a low viral load, I was a good candidate for treatment. Since I was relatively young and my liver was still in pretty good shape, Dr. Hassanein wanted to get me on an experimental program right away.

"Now there will be some side effects," he warned. "You'll be taking a bunch of pills and injecting yourself with interferon every day for a year."

"Injecting myself?" I wasn't sure if I heard right. For someone who hated needles, I couldn't imagine actually pushing one into my upper thigh or abdomen, as he explained I would.

"Don't worry. We'll teach you how," he said encouragingly.

Interferon, I learned, was given at different dosages and in varying frequencies, and often prescribed in combination with an antiviral called ribavirin. The side effects were quite onerous, as I discovered when I started my treatment program.

I'm not going to sugarcoat this. The first few weeks were horrible. After each injection I developed terrible shaking chills, fevers, drenching sweats, and a fatigue that drained all of my energy. For someone who doesn't like needles or pills, I was now compelled to live with both every day for one year.

I was told to drink as much water as I could and try and maintain my weight. This became almost impossible as even my favorite foods started tasting metallic and became unappealing. I finally resorted to protein shakes blended with fruit and ice cream as a way of taking in calories.

Fatigue overwhelmed me. For the first few months of treatment, I found it difficult to work with any effectiveness. On many days, I left the office after lunch and went home to nap for several hours before dinner.

In addition to being tired all of the time and losing weight, I also developed an extreme sensitivity to light, blotchy skin problems, and hair loss. Friends noticed that I looked thin and worn out. Although my doctor encouraged me to keep up my exercise regimen, all I could really do was take slow walks through the neighborhood.

I wasn't much help around the house for four or five months either until my body began to get used to the medications. The new drug trial that I was participating in required a particularly high dose of interferon. As a result, my blood needed to be examined every few weeks. I felt like a pin cushion with all the needles I was being poked with, but I was willing to proceed because Dr. Hassanein assured me that it was going to give me the best possible chance of getting rid of the virus.

During my lowest moments, however, I fought waves of depression. The thought of hanging in there for a whole year was daunting, especially since there was no guarantee of success. Was it all going to be in vain?

I didn't know.

I recalled what I had learned from my previous illness and from reading about POW survivors in Vietnam and how they had endured for years in brutally horrible conditions. They managed to persevere through horrible circumstances by breaking time down into bite-sized increments, by setting small achievable goals, by learning to lean on each other especially when they were most vulnerable, by discovering a tenacious inner strength they didn't know they possessed, and by relying on a faith that may have been latent—but blossomed—during their trials. I decided consciously to try to employ similar strategies as I continued through my treatment.

I also sought encouragement from others who had successfully overcome their battle with hepatitis C. I began communicating with optimistic Thelma Thiel, the founder of the Hepatitis Foundation International, and hearing firsthand from other patients.

It all helped, but my treatment really turned out to be my year from hell.

ABOVE THE FOLD

Several months into my treatment program, I decided to call Tom Cushman, a columnist with the *San Diego Union-Tribune* that I had known over the years and whom I respected greatly. My purpose was to tell Tom—and readers of San Diego's largest newspaper—that there were many people like myself in our own community who are also infected with hepatitis C but who don't know it or, may know it, but were too embarrassed to do anything about it.

My previous experience with ulcerative colitis had taught me that I had a unique platform to raise the visibility of a disease and perhaps help people talk more openly about this hidden illness. Hepatitis C had become very stigmatized due to the fact that it was mostly connected with IV drug users, and no one wanted to be associated with that. This had to change if we were going to make any headway in confronting this disease.

Tom listened as I described the events of the last few months and then wrote a compelling and informative story that was played above the fold on page one of the front news section.

"Benirschke's hope is that by personalizing the disease with a name familiar in San Diego, some in the at-risk category will be encouraged to undergo testing that may detect hepatitis C," Cushman wrote.

I pointed out that the road to the doctor's office is always paved with good intentions, but hepatitis C was too dangerous a disease to take lightly. I noted that I was forced again to appreciate the value of life and how precious family and friends were. Since I now had a wife and family, the fight to stay alive was no longer just about me—it was about all of us.

During this very challenging time, I was committed to not missing a treatment and finishing the protocol just as it was designed. The therapy was working and during my routine blood checks, the virus had become undetectable. I was thrilled and even celebrated with Mary after my last injection. There was an emerging belief that if a patient was still clear of the virus six months after treatment, then he or she would be considered cured. So now it was wait and see.

Unfortunately, a month later after a blood test, I got the bad news that the virus had come back. I was heartbroken and really discouraged. All of the pain and suffering and the diligence to not miss a dose seemed for naught. The yearlong effort hadn't just been hard on me but especially on Mary and the family. I was devastated.

My physician tried to console me. "Rolf, you need to know that your liver got a chance to rest and recover for a full year, stop the progression of the disease, and perhaps even begin to repair itself. When you're ready, I'd like you to consider another treatment based on a different kind of interferon that is just being tested," Dr. Hassanein said.

After marshaling my reserves and talking things over with Mary, I committed to another yearlong journey of interferon shots and antiviral pills with the same difficult side effects. There would be days when I would drag myself home from work, skip dinner with the family, and go straight to bed. Even when I wasn't working, I was usually tired and irritable. Mary was left to manage the four kids as best she could while I felt useless and a burden. It was a very challenging time for all of us.

I lost another fifteen pounds, but my spirits were buoyed once again by the reports that my viral load had become undetectable shortly after starting treatment. With that knowledge, it made the decision to continue to fight through the frustrating side effects month after month easier. Unfortunately, when my year of treatment was over, the hepatitis C virus returned once again. I was now a two-time loser, worn out and more discouraged than ever. I needed to take a break, and my family needed time to recover. The physical and mental stress of worrying about my health and what it was doing to Mary and the kids was awful.

But life moves on, so we picked up the pieces and focused our attention on raising our kids, while I remained especially diligent about not inadvertently infecting anyone in the family. I maintained regular checkups with Dr. Hassanein, who was still upbeat and reminded me continually that even though the treatments had failed, they had given my liver "a rest." So long as I remained committed to not drinking even a single glass of wine, there were promising new treatments on the horizon, he said.

Five years after my second treatment failed, Dr. Hassanein told me about a new pegylated-interferon therapy that was showing more promising results. In clinical trials, about 50 percent of patients were experiencing success, and he suggested I try it.

Once again, I talked through the pros and cons with Mary, and I asked myself if I was ready to put myself through another arduous treatment program. We decided to go for it. This time, the yearlong treatment regimen worked. I was cured! I was finally free of the virus and the dark cloud that had been hanging over my life for eight years. The gratitude I felt toward Dr. Hassanein and the new treatment protocol left me overwhelmed and incredibly grateful that pharmaceutical companies had continued to search for better and more effective treatments.

That gratefulness would turn into a new mission as I entered the "fourth quarter" of my life.

20

FINAL EXTRA POINT

After finally becoming cured of hepatitis C and having the chance to reflect on the journey my life had taken and the health detours I had been forced to travel, a new mission for my life began to take shape. I started to think about how I might be able to devote the rest of my life to educating, encouraging, and supporting others who were facing their own difficult health challenges.

By now, I'd visited hundreds of patients in various hospitals in San Diego over the years, and I'd spoken on the phone with countless others across the country and internationally who were dealing with Crohn's disease, ulcerative colitis, ostomy surgery, and hepatitis C. I'd written two additional books—*Great Comebacks from Ostomy Surgery* and *Embracing Life*—that featured inspirational stories of people who not only survived but thrived following ostomy surgery.

Following my nearly ten-year battle with hepatitis C, I came to realize that I felt most fulfilled when speaking with all kinds of patients, their families, and the doctors and nurses who had treated them. I felt comfortable raising public awareness for these difficult-to-talk-about illnesses and looked for every opportunity to speak or do interviews with the media. I felt increasingly drawn to finding ways to help by sharing my experiences as well as all that I had learned from the many patients I had spoken with—from writing a note of encouragement, to sending a book, to speaking out as a patient advocate (which I would later do in front of the U.S. Congress).

As I became more and more drawn to the medical community, I began to dream about how I might serve as a liaison between the patient and the health-care world, amplify the voices of patients, help them to become more engaged in their health care, and in the process, improve their experiences and the outcomes of their treatments.

One thing led to another, and in 2009, I overcame my self-doubt about never having gone to graduate school or having been formally educated on how to build a business. With a great friend, Greg Anton, we took a leap of faith and co-founded Legacy Health Strategies, a company dedicated to supporting, educating, and inspiring patients who face many different health challenges.

We took the coping skills and strategies I'd learned from my own health experiences, the thousands of patients I'd connected with over the years, and the learnings of many engagement and behavior modification experts and developed proprietary Patient Assessment Technology (PAT™) and JOURNEY Learning™ methodologies as part of the Legacy Care Model™. This allows us to scale and support large numbers of patients in many different disease states concurrently.

The first concept that patients must learn is how to break time down into bite-sized increments. You have to literally figure out how to get through the day—perhaps the next hour—and not allow yourself to worry about tomorrow or a week from now.

The second idea is that patients have to learn how to set small, achievable goals. You remember my mailbox story and what happened after I got home from the hospital following my ostomy surgery. My goal each morning was to get up out of bed—no small task as weak as I was—and walk to my neighbor's mailbox and back to the house. Each day I would add another mailbox to my route, and before long I found myself shuffling up and down the entire length of the street.

The goal of adding a mailbox each day sounded simple, but it was *my* goal. Every time I accomplished that goal, I felt a little better and knew I was heading in the right direction. The power of achieving— even something seemingly insignificant to others—was very real and very powerful to me.

The next thing I was forced to learn was the importance of swallowing my pride and allowing myself to lean on others . . . to accept their help. That's not as easy as it sounds because many of us are used to being able to handle things on our own and we have a hard time asking for help. We're embarrassed to let others know what is really going on, so we shut ourselves in and just try to figure it all out ourselves.

When American soldiers were held captive in Hanoi during the Vietnam War, many survived because they were *forced* to lean on each other. A hierarchy of command was informally set up in the prison camps where the highest-ranking captive officer assumed leadership responsibility for the other prisoners. It was up to him to keep his troops together and motivated and not let anyone lose hope or give up when times got tough, when food was denied, when beatings were increased, and when prisoners became sick.

If he heard that one of his men was really struggling and couldn't seem to take it anymore, he would pass the word along and other prisoners would find ways to encourage their compatriot. They'd cough in code and tap messages on the walls of the adjoining cells. They'd leave notes where they would be found by their ailing comrade with words of encouragement: *We're in this together . . . hang in there. . . they're not going to beat us . . . you can do this . . . we're here for you!*

When I was sick, it felt like I wanted to quit a hundred times, but my friends and my family and my teammates wouldn't let me. They wouldn't give up on me even when I was ready to give up on myself. Instead, they'd talk their way into my off-limits hospital room to sit and cry with me, to hold my hand and pray. They'd come by and take me for a drive after I'd been released from the hospital and could hardly walk. They'd come and visit with me in the backyard of my parent's house when I couldn't get out of the lawn chair without help. And when I had a pity party and wondered if life was worth living with two ostomy bags attached to my side, they let me share my fears . . . every single one of them.

I wondered out loud, "Tell me why I should want to live? What kind of life can I possibly have? My whole life revolves around sports and outdoor activities, and now I don't think I'll be able to play any of them. And returning to the NFL? Are you kidding me? With two bags on my side? No way! Nobody's ever played in the NFL with a bag before. There's no way I'll ever be able to kick again!"

And what about traveling out of town, visiting a foreign country, or going back to Africa like I had dreamed of?

"Not a chance," I lamented. "I'll never travel again."

And girls. I liked girls and had always wanted to get married and have a partner to share my life with and raise a family with.

"Who will ever marry me? Look at me. There's no way!" And that's when I would start to tear up.

The more I voiced the deep-seated fears I had buried deep in my mind, the more discouraged and depressed I became. I had done a good job of getting through each day one at a time, but now that it became clear I was going to live, those fears began to overwhelm me . . . but not my friends and family. They let me talk and cry, and they shared my heartbreak. They empathized with my situation, but they wouldn't let me give into it. The reality was that my situation wouldn't change. I was stuck wearing two bags, there was nothing anybody could do about that, and it did no good to continue to whine about it. What would have to change was my *attitude about my situation.*

As I slowly recovered and began to heal and put on weight, I wrestled through the five steps of grieving. I went from denial and isolation to anger, past bargaining straight to a deep depression, and finally to acceptance.

I came to realize that I was lucky to be alive and began to embrace that fact and appreciate it with every new day, with every walk on the beach, with every sunset, and with every kind friend or stranger who went out of their way to encourage me. I began to experience a joy that was hard to explain because my circumstances hadn't changed at all.

As I accepted my "new normal" and began to fight back, I discovered that my fears were like "dragons of doubt" that can paralyze a person unless they are attacked. In the process I learned that, like dragons, those fears were not real . . . they never materialized.

My mind and body healed, and I returned to the NFL to kick seven more seasons and resumed playing all my favorite sports including tennis, golf, snow skiing, ice hockey, and scuba diving. I went on to travel extensively all over the world—even back to Africa three different times—and got married to the most extraordinary woman anybody could ever ask for and have four amazing kids.

The same can happen for you. It is possible to move from feeling overwhelmed by the negative to choosing to look for the good things that are happening. You can recognize that you're better today than you were a week ago. You can acknowledge that you've put on weight and color has returned to your skin. You can let people in who want to help you. When these things begin to happen, doors start to open that you never could have imagined when you were in the bitter, "poor me" state of mind.

At Legacy Health Strategies, we have the privilege of working with patients and their families and the medical community of doctors, nurses, medical device firms, and pharmaceutical companies that care for them. We help them understand that patients have several important but unspoken questions that must be answered in the affirmative if a caregiver or a company wants to truly connect with them. They are questions like:

- *Can I trust you?*

In other words, is what you are saying true, or are you just trying to sell me something? Are you really looking out for my best interests or your own? Without trust, it is very difficult to develop a relationship with any substance.

- *Do you excel in what you do?*

Are you the best? It's important for a patient to know that their health-care providers are on the cutting edge of the illness, understand the latest research, and can demonstrate their competency. Patients want to know that they are working with the best.

And lastly and maybe most importantly:

- *Do you really care about me as a person?*

Do you know what my hopes and fears are . . . what is important to me? Will you treat me like a person first and a patient second?

At Legacy Health Strategies, we understand patients and caregivers desire support and deserve individualized guidance and coaching throughout their treatment journey. We also understand the power of the patient's voice and how, when that voice is shared and amplified, it can dramatically change the illness experience.

And, maybe most importantly, we have learned the power of hope and how to provide it.

Hope Rising to the Surface

There's a story that I love to tell that illustrates the enormous power of hope. There was a submarine coming back home at the end of World War II. When the sub was surfacing, the vessel accidentally struck a surface ship and started to sink. The captain immediately sent out a May Day alert—an SOS. The Coast Guard was quick to respond, but by the time a cutter arrived on the scene, the sub had sunk to the bottom of a shallow channel.

The Coast Guard quickly deployed divers who dove to the submerged sub. Once they got there, the divers heard a banging on the hull coming from the inside of the submarine. It was a message being delivered by one of the trapped sailors in Morse Code asking the question: *Is there hope?*

One of the first rescue divers to reach the sub quickly banged out a response message back: *Yes, there's hope. Help has arrived. We are here.*

I have learned that you can live thirty days without food, three days without water, and even up to eight minutes without air, but I don't believe you can survive a single second without hope. Hope can come in many ways, but I have learned that it's most powerfully delivered from those of us who have been there, who can say to other patients:

We know what you are going through . . . .

We understand how difficult things are right now, but you CAN make it. You CAN endure because we have endured . . . as have countless others.

We are here to help. There is hope.

This reminds me of a practical lesson I learned when I was a seven-year-old boy growing up in New Hampshire. Every now and then we would get a four-foot snowfall and Dad would ask, "Hey, Rolf, can you go out and get the mail?"

Well, the mailbox was at the end of the long driveway that was piled high with snow. To get there the first time was hard work, trudging through the heavy snow to make a path. But on the second and third day, if my siblings or friends had walked on that same path I had first formed, getting the mail became pretty easy . . . and, of course, it became quite simple if we shoveled the driveway completely.

It's the same way with a health diagnosis crisis. Hearing from someone who has been there, someone who has been on the same journey you're about to embark upon, and who can take the fear out of what lies ahead, can instill great hope.

When you lose hope, you lose the ability to fight. But with hope, you get to discover something special . . . an incredibly powerful force . . . an "indomitable spirit" that I believe God has instilled in each one of us.

Unfortunately, most of us never get to discover this power because we live our lives relatively safely between the guardrails, bouncing from side to side as we encounter different bumps along the road of life. It's not until we "crash" over the guardrails and end up in the "ditch" because of a serious illness or injury, the premature loss of a child, a divorce, the death of a loved one, or any number of life's incredibly difficult circumstances, that we get to discover this spirit.

It seems appropriate here to share a short poem I found years ago that eloquently expresses how I feel after looking back at all that I have gone through. I hope you find inspiration from these thoughts written on a Civil War battlefield.

MOST RICHLY BLESSED

> *I asked God for strength, that I might achieve.*
> *I was made weak, that I might learn humbly to obey.*
> *I asked for health, that I might do greater things.*
> *I was given infirmity, that I might do better things.*
> *I asked for riches, that I might be happy.*
> *I was given poverty, that I might be wise.*
> *I asked for all things, that I might enjoy life.*
> *I was given life, that I might enjoy all things.*
> *I got nothing I asked for, but everything I had hoped for.*
> *Despite myself, my prayers were answered.*
> *I am, among all men, most richly blessed.*
>
> —AN UNKNOWN SOLDIER OF THE CONFEDERACY

So, if you're reading this and find yourself in the "ditch," having "crashed" due to an untimely illness or unplanned tragedy, I hope you will pause and realize you have an amazing opportunity ahead of you.

You have the chance to discover that indomitable spirit that I'm convinced lies dormant inside you—that I believe can only be uncovered when you go through a major crisis. But moving forward requires a decision . . . a decision only you can make. You can receive all the help and support in the world, but you must be willing to commit to taking on this new challenge in front of you. Only then will you have the chance to learn that you have greater courage, a greater ability to cope, greater perseverance, and even more creativity than you ever dreamed you had.

Your life can become changed forever, and instead of just surviving, you can come out of the experience transformed with an entirely new outlook on life. You will live differently. You will appreciate family and friends in a whole new way. You will empathize more, show kindness quicker, take more risks, laugh easier, and live life more fully. You will discover attributes about yourself that one day you'll be able to look back on and say, *If I hadn't gone through that horrible experience, I wouldn't be who I am today or doing what I am doing now. I wouldn't be as self-confident or as capable. I wouldn't be as appreciative, and I wouldn't have learned that a long and pain-free life is not guaranteed to any of us.*

I heard someone say once that wisdom is a tough teacher; she always gives the exam first and teaches the lessons later. So true.

Maybe one day you'll say to yourself: *I'm genuinely thankful for all that I have been forced to endure. I wouldn't trade the pain and anger and heartbreak because of how it has changed me.*

When that happens, you will know that you have passed the test and gained the wisdom, and you will appreciate more than ever being . . . *alive and kicking!*

Acknowledgements

One thing I've learned from playing team sports is that *every* player is critically important if the team is to be successful. As I reflect on the help and emotional support I received in writing and revising *Alive & Kicking*, I feel compelled to share my appreciation as best I can. I am deeply indebted to lots of people, but two who stand out are the love of my life, my wife, Mary, and my partner at Legacy Health Strategies, Greg Anton.

In addition, it was a chance meeting with an old high school acquaintance, Mike Yorkey, that allowed us to put together the story the way I felt called to write it. Without Mike's talent and commitment to the original book and this revision, I'm not sure it would ever have been accomplished.

Although *Alive & Kicking* was written to encourage people facing difficult times, particularly those struggling with inflammatory bowel disease, ostomy surgery, or hepatitis C, it was also a chance for me to tell Mom and Dad, my brother, Steve, and sister, Ingrid, how much they've meant to me. They were incredibly supportive during my toughest times, and I will never forget that. Both my parents are in their nineties and still with us today, and I love them more than I can ever express.

Finally, I'm reminded of a story about a beaver talking to a squirrel while looking up at massive Hoover Dam and explaining, "No, I didn't actually build it, but it is based on an *idea* I had."

Our team at Legacy Health Strategies has taken my ideas and all I have learned from the thousands of patients I have connected with over the years and built a "Hoover Dam" of a company, so we can scale our efforts and support patients dealing with a wide variety of serious health challenges. For their passion, commitment, and encouragement, I'm eternally grateful and offer my sincerest thanks and deepest gratitude.

INVITE ROLF BENIRSCHKE TO SPEAK AT YOUR NEXT CORPORATE OR COMMUNITY EVENT

Rolf Benirschke is a compelling storyteller and inspiring speaker whose humble and conversational style connects immediately with his audiences. While sharing his own journey of health challenges and the many trials he has experienced over the years, Rolf is a master at tailoring his message to connect with a variety of audiences, showing others ways to overcome some of life's most challenging circumstances and discover their own indomitable spirit while leaving a legacy of hope wherever he goes.

Rolf routinely speaks at national sales meetings, before major corporations, and at health-related events across the country. Some of his past some of his past engagements have included UCSD Healthcare System, Kaiser Permanente, Dartmouth Hitchcock Medical Center, the Centers for Disease Control and Prevention, Biocom, AdvaMed, The Hartford, AbbVie, Nanogen, WOC Nurses, YPO groups, and many others.

If you, your business, or community organization would like Rolf to speak at your event, you can reach him at:

Legacy Health Strategies
12790 El Camino Real, Suite 300
San Diego, CA 92130
(858) 568-7555 office
www.rolfbenirschke.com
rolf@legacyhealthstrategies.com

For Bulk Purchases of *Alive & Kicking* and Other Books by Rolf Benirschke

If you're interested in making bulk purchases of *Alive & Kicking*, please contact:

Rolf Benirschke Enterprises
12790 El Camino Real, Suite 300
San Diego, CA 92130
(858) 259-2092 office
www.rolfbenirschke.com

In addition, Rolf Benirschke has authored two other books:

Great Comebacks from Ostomy Surgery
Fifteen people who have survived and thrived following ostomy surgery share their heart-wrenching and heartwarming stories about how they dealt with challenging circumstances that led to their ostomy surgeries . . . and how they redeemed their lives.

Embracing Life
In this follow-up resource to *Alive & Kicking* and *Great Comebacks from Ostomy Surgery*, twelve others share their inspiring comeback stories. Anyone going through the struggles of inflammatory bowel disease or facing ostomy surgery will be moved and encouraged by this book.

Visit Rolf's website at www.rolfbenirschke.com to order any of Rolf's books (which are also available in ebook versions) and www.legacyhealthstrategies.com to learn more about the work he is doing for patients with medical device and pharmaceutical companies, and health systems around the country.

About the Authors

Rolf Benirschke is a former placekicker for the San Diego Chargers, having played in the National Football League for ten seasons from 1977-1986. He retired with sixteen team records and as the third most-accurate kicker in NFL history. Rolf received numerous honors including NFL Man of the Year, NFL Comeback Player of the Year, and NFL Players Association Hero of the Year. He became the twentieth player to be inducted into the San Diego Chargers Hall of Fame in 1997, and in 1999 he was inducted into the San Diego Hall of Champions.

Today, Rolf devotes most of his time to Legacy Health Strategies, a strategic planning and marketing company he co-founded. Legacy partners with medical device and pharmaceutical companies, pharmacy benefit managers and payers, and health systems to develop patient support and adherence programs that build patient communities and help patients stay compliant on their treatment plans. He also remains a sought-after inspirational speaker around the country.

Rolf and his wife, Mary, are the parents of four children: Erik, Kari, Timmy, and Ryan, and continue to live in the San Diego area.

You can learn more about Rolf and his activities at: www.rolfbenirschke.com.

Mike Yorkey, a veteran author, editor, and collaborator of more than one hundred books, has known Rolf since high school when they attended La Jolla High School together.

He has collaborated with KKLA talk show host Frank Sontag in *Light the Way Home*; Oakland A's Ben Zobrist and his wife, Julianna, a Christian music artist, in *Double Play*; Washington Redskins quarterback Colt McCoy and his father, Brad, in *Growing Up Colt*; San Francisco Giants pitcher Dave Dravecky in *Called Up*; tennis star Michael Chang in *Holding Serve*; and paralyzed Rutgers' defensive tackle Eric LeGrand in *Believe: My Faith and the Tackle That Changed My Life.*

Mike is also the co-author of the internationally bestselling *Every Man's Battle* series with Steve Arterburn and Fred Stoeker and is the co-author of three fiction titles, including *Chasing Mona Lisa.*

His website is www.mikeyorkey.com.